THE RATZ

SIMON ADORIAN
CECILY O'NEILL

Acknowledgements

The authors and publisher would like to thank the following for permission to reproduce illustrations and photographs:
Mick Moore, main front cover photograph, back cover photograph; Peter Schouten, inset front cover photograph, title page; Tim Beer, pages 62–69, 73; Dave Sumner, pages 70, 87; Steve Fricker, pages 74–75; Popperfoto, page 78; Allsport/Simon Bruty, page 83; Tessa Mangion/Karen Staples, page 90

Published by CollinsEducational
An imprint of HarperCollins*Publishers*
77–85 Fulham Palace Road
Hammersmith
London W6 8JB

ISBN 0 00 330301 2

First published in 1991

Designed by Dave Sumner
Photoset in Linotron Century Schoolbook by
Northern Phototypesetting Company Ltd., Bolton
Printed by Bell & Bain, Thornliebank, Glasgow

HOW TO USE THE PLAY

The Ratz is based on the legend of the Pied Piper of Hamelin, but places the same dilemmas in a more contemporary context. The play arose out of a series of drama workshops involving pupils, parents and friends of St Leonard's School in Dorset. Through role-play and improvisation, the actors developed the characters and the action of every scene in the play – and a few outside of it!

You can use the play text and the accompanying extension material in a number of ways. Here are some of the possibilities:

● Read the play text. Use the script and extension material as a lead-in to workshops in drama.

● Work towards a group production of the play. Build in ideas and scenes arising from your work on the extension material. Share some of your work informally with other groups, or in a school assembly.

● Extend your group work into a more ambitious production involving an extended cast.

From time to time, as you read the play, you will come across a sign like this: ⌐91⟩

Each signpost will direct you to a section of the extension material which relates to the scene you are reading. There you will find suggestions for developing the scene.

CAST

Hamelin Town Council
Henry Stott-Stickland, Lord Mayor

Councillor Witham	Councillor Mrs Phipp
Councillor Fitzpatrick	Councillor Mrs Grahame
Councillor Miss Worthington	Councillor Ms Fortune

Citizens of Hamelin
All ranks and professions are represented among the Citizens, e.g. a nurse, a vicar, a bus driver, a shop manager, a lawyer etc. The Citizens can be placed among the play's audience. At key points of the play the whole audience is addressed as the populace of Hamelin.

Mrs Stride	Mr Bind
Mr Sparks	Reverend Crouch
Miss Callow	PC Luckless
Mrs Wright	Towncrier

The Inventors and other townspeople

Children of Hamelin

James	Jenny	
Paul	Kate	Kevin
Lorna	Jo	Becky

Jan – has had a disability since birth which affects his legs. He has never been able to run and play with the other children.

The Ratz
A subculture from the long neglected East Side of town. In recent weeks gangs of Ratz have raided the respectable centre of Hamelin. Ratz speak in a dialect of their own, completely meaningless to ordinary citizens. In production, Ratz will need to develop tribal rituals and their own range of sounds, shouts, whistles and shrieks. Lines **printed like this** need to be translated into 'Ratspeak'.

The Stranger
No name, no roots, no allies. No one is even certain if the Stranger is male or female.

SCENE 1 ●
TAKEN OFF BY THE RATZ

The Town Square.

Jan *alone in the centre. He is sketching in a notebook, completely absorbed.*

The silence is broken by shouts and the sound of people running. The **Children** *burst into the square playing 'tag'. They use the whole area, going in and out of the audience using scenery, seats etc. as playground equipment.* **Jan** *remains still at the centre.*

Eventually the game slows down. **James** *is 'it'. He singles out* **Kate** *as his target. She shrieks excitedly then hides behind* **Jan**, *keeping him between herself and* **James**. **James** *circles menacingly, while* **Kate** *rotates* **Jan**. *The other children watch spellbound, absolutely still.*

Jan *shrugs off* **Kate** *forcefully. She steps back. Then* **James** *lunges forward and 'tags'* **Jan**.

JAMES	You're it.
JAN	Not playing.
KATE	Got to. You're it.
JAN	Forget it.
JAMES	Come on, everyone. Jan's it.
CHILDREN	Jan's it . . . Jan's it . . . Jan's it . . . Jan's it . . .

As they chant, the **Children** *dart around* **Jan** *daring him to 'tag' them.* **Jan** *does not budge. Gradually, the* **Children** *stop and the chant fades out.*

JENNY	That's it. – spoil our game. I would.
JAN	I'm not spoiling anything. Just carry on. Only don't ask me to join in.
KEVIN	Why not?
JAN	Look, I just don't want to, all right?
JENNY	Forget it, he'll never join in now. You know what he's like.
LORNA	We can ask.
JAMES	All right. (*to* **Paul**) You ask him, Paul. You go to

1

	his school. You used to be his friend.
PAUL	Come on, Jan.
JAN	Look . . . I can't, can I?
PAUL	It'll be all right with your leg. It doesn't matter.
JAN	*(savagely)* Doesn't matter to WHO? *(pause)* Doesn't matter that I could never catch up with any of you lot? Doesn't matter that you're only *letting* me play? Doesn't matter that I'd only spoil the whole game? No, I won't be a good sport just so you can all laugh at me. You can count me out.

Long, embarrassed silence

PAUL	I told you what he's like. He'll never play.
CHILDREN	Boring . . . typical.
KATE	So what is he doing then?
LORNA	I expect he's waiting for Becky to show.
KEVIN	Yeah . . . Becky.
JAN	So?
JO	Waiting for Becky are we?

*The **Children** tease **Jan** but he ignores them.*

LORNA	Look. He's got his precious little black book with him again.

*The **Children** start to circle **Jan**. He is looking in his book.*

JENNY	Wonder what he's drawing now.
PAUL	I expect he's writing something about us.
JO	Only one way to find out.
JAMES	Let's have a look, Jan.
JAN	No.
JENNY	Come on. *(She grabs the book.)* Thanks, Jan.
JAMES	Here, Jenny, pass.

Jenny *throws the book to **James**. The **Children** start to throw it to one another, with **Jan** 'piggy in the middle'. They tease him, waving the book at him, inviting him to come and get it. **Jan** tries clumsily to get the book, but can't.*

2

Enter **Becky**

BECKY	*(shouts)* Cut it out, you lot. You – give him his book back. You should know better than that, what with his leg.
JENNY	Yes sir! Anything you say, Becky!
JAMES	I reckon he's asking for it. If he'd just joined in for once, none of this would've happened. He winds people up, if you ask me. *(Leaves)*
PAUL	No point staying now.
LORNA	Well, I've got to be back before it's dark, anyway. 'Cos of the Ratz.
JO	Me too.

The **Children** *all drift out in different directions, moaning about* **Jan**, *saying* 'see you' *etc. to each other.*

Silence. **Becky** *gives* **Jan** *the book.*

JAN	Thanks, Beck.
BECKY	Why do you let them do it to you, Jan?
JAN	I can't help it, can I?
BECKY	What was it this time?
JAN	The usual. School, home, out here in the street, it's always the same. It's 'Let's get Jan'.
BECKY	But what actually happened this time?
JAN	Oh, they all come charging in like – like they was Ratz – and then expect me to join in their poxy game.
BECKY	And?
JAN	And when I said I didn't want to, they all started picking on me.
BECKY	And why didn't you join in? Well?
JAN	Don't you start as well.
BECKY	They don't mean bad, Jan. They're only trying to help.
JAN	Help? It's not *help* I want. Look, d'you think I don't know what their parents tell them? 'Be nice to the cripple boy now, won't you? We know it's not much fun to always have him trailing after you and messing up your play, but do be nice to him. Just think yourselves lucky to be fit and

3

	healthy and not like *that*. And then it's the mother we feel sorry for. First that boy – and heaven knows he's not an easy child – and now having to bring him up on her own.' Oh, Becky do you think I don't know what they say?
BECKY	It's not as simple as that, Jan, and you know it. You can't go on forever using that leg as an excuse to stay on the outside.

Jan *shrugs, scribbles in his book.*

	Just for once, eh? Maybe if you joined in, then people would accept you more. Instead of always keeping your distance with that book of yours. What're you writing in it now, Jan?
JAN	Just . . . stuff.
BECKY	Let me have a look.
JAN	No . . . it's private.
BECKY	Go on, you said I was your one true friend, didn't you? Then you shouldn't keep a secret from me. Come on.
JAN	Look. I don't want to show you or anyone else. OK?

Long, embarrassed silence

BECKY	Oh, did I tell you about what happened to our dog?
JAN	*(concerned)* No – what?
BECKY	It disappeared.
JAN	*(worried)* What happened?
BECKY	Nothing much – don't worry. It came back the next day but we was dead scared, what with all this talk about the Ratz coming up West and people's animals going missing and that.
JAN	I'm glad. My dog did that once.
BECKY	I never knew you had a dog.
JAN	I don't. But we used to. When Dad was with us. It was brilliant. Called Sam. But when Dad went, Mum just got rid of it, without even asking me.
BECKY	Why don't you ask if you can have another one?
JAN	Huh.

4

| BECKY | You could ask her, Jan. It might work. |
| JAN | No point. You know what she's like. |

'Ratmusic'. Flashing lights, strobe etc.
The **Ratz** *burst in from all directions, hissing, shrieking, yelling, whistling etc. They use every part of the area as they charge through the audience – over, under, through any obstacles of the set.*

91>

Music stops. **Rat 1** *whistles.* **Ratz** *freeze.*

Rat 2 *yells* **Oy!***. He points at* **Becky***. The* **Ratz** *stare at her, occasionally making threatening noises.* **Rat 1** *whistles. Five of the* **Ratz** *form a tight circle around* **Becky** *so she cannot escape.*

Rat 3 *shouts. All the* **Ratz** *scream, whistle, whoop and chant* **Oy. . . oy. . . oy. . . oy. . .** *as they rush* **Becky** *out of the Square.*

| JAN | *(limps to centre and screams)* No-o-o-o-o-o. |

Blackout

SCENE 2 ●
A PUBLIC MEETING

The Town Hall.

Houselights on. Table with seven seats behind it set on a stage at one end of the hall. The **Citizens** *sit among the audience.*

As the **Councillors** *make their way towards the stage, they greet friends amongst the* **Citizens** *and amongst the real audience, smiling and waving.*

Once all seven **Councillors** *are seated at the table, the* **Mayor** *asks them all* 'Are you ready?' *and eventually bangs down the gavel and asks for order.*

MAYOR   Could I have your attention please? Ladies and gentlemen, on behalf of the Hamelin Town Council may I extend a very warm welcome to you all. It's very encouraging to see such a good turn-out for this public meeting. Now, we all know why we are here tonight – to discuss what we as a town can possibly do about the problem of the Ratz.

Murmurs of assent from the **Citizens**

In recent weeks these gangs have become much bolder about coming up from the East Side into the centre of town, and now this week we have had this dreadful business of a missing child. We – *your* Council – are here tonight to listen to you. We value and respect your opinions greatly and hope that as a community we can tackle this problem together.

Ironic cheers from some **Citizens**

Before we start to take questions and speeches from the floor, each Councillor will have the opportunity to introduce themselves and make a brief statement on the Ratz issue. Then it will be

	over to you. I am already known to a great many of you – Henry Stott-Stickland, your Lord Mayor, Chairman of the Chamber of Trade and Commerce and also Chairman of Stott-Stickland and Sons, Purveyors of Quality Groceries.
1st CITIZEN	Get on with it.
MAYOR	Indeed I expect there are many of you who also remember my father who was Lord Mayor some 20 years ago . . .
2nd CITIZEN	Yeah, and a fat lot of good he was too.
MAYOR	. . . and I am proud to think that I am continuing the fine family tradition of public service. And now, I should like to introduce to you Councillor Witham.
WITHAM	Good evening. Councillor Witham, Chairman of the Town Improvements Committee and a Councillor for the past 13 years. I'll make no bones about the fact that I believe that it is our duty as a town to . . . er . . . eliminate the Ratz as efficiently and humanely as possible. *(mixed reaction from* **Citizens***)* These hooligans, not content with the squalor and poverty of the East Side, seem hell-bent on bringing it with them into *our* part of the town. The sooner we act the better. The damage already done is bad enough – our Town Improvements Committee will now have to start on a major redecoration programme, cleaning off graffiti, repainting signs, replacing smashed windows and dealing with some terrible bumps in the pavements which I trip up over every morning.
3rd CITIZEN	Aaaah . . . shame.

Witham *sits down to mixed reaction, and* **Mayor** *beckons to* **Fortune** *to stand and speak.*

FORTUNE	Hi . . . I'm Councillor Liz Fortune. I am a social worker based in the East Side of town, and I am currently Chairperson of the Recreation and Amenities Committee. I have been on the Town Council for the last two years, representing the Hamelin East ward, and I believe that the only way we are ever going to solve the problem of the

Ratz is through long-term investment by the Council in community projects and local business.

Angry reaction from some **Citizens**

CITIZENS	*(at same time)* What good's that gonna do? Don't talk wet. You're not living in the real world. Rubbish!
FORTUNE	Poor housing, inadequate sewerage and drainage, no health care and no jobs – that's what causes Ratz. This problem has been with us for years. Now it's crawled out of the slums up into the west of town, suddenly our citizens are getting angry. No real notice was taken of the problem until the very serious matter of a child being taken off by the Ratz.
4th CITIZEN	Shame!
FORTUNE	Well I say that if proper notice had been taken sooner – by people like *you*, *(to* **4th Citizen***)* yes *you* sir – then maybe that child would be safe right now.

Fortune *sits down. Uproar in the hall. Cries of* 'Shame' *etc.* **Mayor** *beckons to* **Fitzpatrick***.*

FITZPATRICK	Good evening, ladies and gentlemen. I am Councillor Fitzpatrick and I am Chairman of the Public Health Committee. I have been a Councillor for 16 years. I hardly need to say that Miss Fortune's speech has been a complete disgrace. She is using the very real tragedy of that child and our town's crisis over the Ratz to make a cheap political point. Yes, I admit that the East Side is in a state of decay. But spending money on it now will just be throwing good money after bad. If we were to spend public funds – *your* taxes, ladies and gentlemen – on fancy schools and hospitals in the East, the Ratz will tear them apart as soon as we've finished. And then where will we be? We have wasted quite enough time on these hooligans that are plastering our walls with graffiti, slashing tyres,

smashing windows and desecrating public
buildings. What we want to do is get the lot of
them put away and then we'll have an end to our
problems. You mark my words.

Fitzpatrick *sits down to applause, boos etc.* **Mayor** *signals to*
Worthington *that it is her turn.*

WORTHINGTON　Hello. My name is Frances Worthington. I
have been a Councillor in Hamelin for 15 years
and I have lived here all my life. As well as being
a member of the Council I am also on the
Education Board. Quite frankly, I feel that we
should give the Ratz a chance.

Uproar in the audience

CITIZENS　*(all at the same time)* Do us a favour, missus.
Give them a chance – the Ratz?
What planet are you from?

WORTHINGTON　No, I really mean it. Why don't we try to
encourage the Ratz to be integrated into local
schools and make friends? Then they would be
able to get jobs because they would have some
qualifications behind them. But instead we are
rejecting them. They are our fellow creatures
but you are treating them like animals.

4th CITIZEN　They are animals.

WORTHINGTON　They are NOT.

Worthington *sits down, still shouting back at hecklers. When the noise*
dies down, **Mayor** *nods to* **Grahame**. *She stands up nervously.*

GRAHAME　Good evening, ladies and gentlemen. I am Mrs
Grahame and I have been on the Council for 11
years now. I am the Chairman of Policy and
Resources. I think this whole business of these
horrible vandals has gone on far too long. I mean,
really, it's spoiling the town. Somehow it's got to
stop. Perhaps we could introduce conscription?
Or something like that? Anyway, I'm looking
forward to hearing some of your ideas. The
Council will listen carefully to your points of view
and simply decide what to do. Thank you.

Grahame *sits down. Muted applause.* **Mayor** *nods to* **Phipp**.

PHIPP	Good evening, ladies and gentlemen. My name is Deirdre Phipp and I am Chairman of our Public Parks and Highways Committee. The matter of the Ratz has been brought to my attention a lot recently. I'm particularly distressed to have found out about one recent occurrence – a bunch of these rebellious vandals were in Rosemont Park and actually went so far as to throw three of our attractive civic benches into the ornamental fountain.
1st CITIZEN	*(sarcastically)* Oh dear . . . *what* a shame!
PHIPP	Furthermore they went on to destroy a large number of plants and shrubs. *(more jeers and ironic comments from* **Citizens***)* Hamelin has long been famous for its gracious architecture and attractive parks. Tourists come from far and wide to visit our town and for occasions like the Lord Mayor's Procession. We cannot let the Ratz spoil our fine town and its traditions. The Ratz are nothing short of vandals and should be locked away for life.

Phipp *sits down to mixed reaction.* **Mayor** *rises to speak.*

MAYOR	Well, there you have it ladies and gentlemen. I'm sure you can see the high level of care and concern felt by your Council. We will now open the discussion to the public.

The **Mayor** *now chairs the public meeting.*

	Yes. You, madam. The lady over there in the nurse's uniform.
STRIDE	Thank you. My name is Sandra Stride and I am a Ward Sister in the District Hospital. We're really at the sharp end of all this, having to deal with all the victims of this recent violence. I want to put a question to Councillor Fitzpatrick, Chairman of the Public Health Committee. When was the last time he was in any of our hospitals?
FITZPATRICK	Well, madam, it so happens that I attended a function at the District Hospital only last month.

STRIDE	Last month! Have you seen the state of some of the people who have been coming in recently, because of all this violence?
FORTUNE	Excuse me, madam, but how do you know that these people have been injured by the Ratz?
STRIDE	*(shouting)* Of course I know, you stupid woman!

Uproar in the crowd

FORTUNE	Yes, but do you have any proof?
STRIDE	*(still shouting)* Proof? It's obvious, isn't it? Wake up, will you? And when did you last visit that hospital?
FORTUNE	*(shouting back)* I work there. I'm in there every Tuesday morning, so don't give me that!
MAYOR	Order! Order! Really this is most unnecessary. Now, can we have another speaker please? Yes, you sir.
BIND	My name's Arthur Bind and what I want to know is what are the Council going to do about all this? It's all very well calling meetings and making speeches, and such like, but meanwhile it goes on. I've had five windows smashed in the last fortnight. I can't afford to go on replacing them, can I?
GRAHAME	Sir, that is precisely why we are holding this meeting. So we can listen to everyone's views and then come to some decision. There is a Council meeting tomorrow.
1st CITIZEN	And a lot of good that will be.

Laughter and jeers

SPARKS	I'm Ron Sparks and I've been living and working in this town all my life and I don't mind telling you, I'm sick of this whole flipping Ratz business. As far as I'm concerned they're vandals and they should be strung up! *(loud cheers from some* **Citizens***)* It's all right for them Councillors in their posh houses as far away from the East Side as they can possibly get. There's no Ratz where *they* live. It's not *their* houses what are getting trashed. It's not *their* cars what get nicked. It's

not *their* windows being put in!

Cheers from most **Citizens**

MAYOR   Order! Order! Please! Believe you me, sir, you do have my sympathy.

SPARKS   Sorry, pal, sympathy ain't enough.

More cheers and laughter from **Citizens**

MAYOR   Another question, please. Ah, I see that the Reverend Crouch has his hand up. Perhaps he can say something to . . . er . . . smooth the ruffled feathers here.

CROUCH   Yes, yes. I feel we need to find a way to live with these Ratz.

3rd CITIZEN   Do us a favour, Reverend. Sit down, will you?

CROUCH   Please. Let me have my say. I somehow feel that if we were to give the Ratz better housing then they might give a bit more respect to the town and its people. And we all need to find a way to talk to each other instead of *at* each other. Then maybe we could find a way to live together peacefully in Hamelin.

PHIPP   Sir, I respect your point of view, of course. But you say 'living peacefully'. Is that *really* what the Ratz want? To 'cooperate'? I think not!

Cheers and shouting from the audience

MAYOR   Order! Order! Yes, the young lady down there.

CALLOW   Yes, my name's Kit Callow and I just want to say that I reckon there's too much fuss about the Ratz. The whole issue is being exaggerated something chronic. Any bit of crime or vandalism in this town and the blame is landed on the Ratz, even when there's no proof. They're just young people having fun. They're not doing nothing!

FITZPATRICK   Not doing nothing! Plastering walls with graffiti, letting down tyres, smashing windows, stealing children – that's not what I call not doing nothing.

12

CALLOW	Just because the Ratz come from the East, it doesn't mean they're all bad. They're just young people having fun – and there's not much fun to be had in *this* town. Maybe the young girl wanted to go with the Ratz.

Most **Citizens** *are outraged at this suggestion.*

2nd CITIZEN	Has it occurred to anyone that the poor parents of that young girl might well be here tonight, sitting among us? Think how they must feel to hear people talking like this.

Long silence

1st CITIZEN	Have any of you Councillors seen the state of our children's play areas recently? You can't take your kids down there without seeing Ratz climbing over all the equipment, shouting and chucking things.
4th CITIZEN	And what about the swimming pool?

At this point all the **Citizens** *are shouting demands,* 'What about the . . .?' *etc. The meeting is breaking down. Suddenly silence is regained by a sharp blast on a police whistle.*

MAYOR	Another question. Yes, Inspector Luckless.
LUCKLESS	I simply wish to draw it to people's attention that we need a larger police force if we are to police this town effectively. At the moment everyone in the town is crying out for firmer law and order, looking to us in the police force, and we are being starved of funds. We just don't have enough policemen where it matters, out there on the streets.
WORTHINGTON	Ah, yes. But of course expanding the police force will be a great drain on public resources. Is that really our first priority?
LUCKLESS	Do you realise how many policemen I have at that station? *Six* policemen, yes *six* . . .

Mrs Wright *stands and waits for silence. She speaks quietly, with a measured assurance.*

WRIGHT	The Ratz come from the East Side of this town. Many of us live in or near the East Side. *You* live in the West part. So – how does this issue affect you? More important, what are you going to do?
MAYOR	We are trying.
WRIGHT	Trying's not good enough. We want action.
SPARKS	Yes, we want action!
CITIZENS	WE WANT ACTION! WE WANT ACTION! WE WANT ACTION! WE WANT ACTION!

Chant continues till blackout. Then silence.

SCENE 3 ●
A STRANGER SPEAKS

The Town Hall. As before.

Spotlight discovers the **Stranger** *sitting casually on the table used by the Council for a public meeting. The* **Councillors** *are still there, 'frozen' in position. The* **Stranger** *has one foot up on the table and surveys the room and the audience with a cold and measured calmness.*

After a long pause, the **Stranger** *starts to speak.*

STRANGER   Welcome to Hamelin.

And *what* an interesting town it is too. Fine Council, for a start. They certainly seem to have the people's best interests at heart. Just the right people to lead a town out of a crisis.

But then, who was it who put them there?

And the citizens. So much to say for yourselves. And all the time you haven't come one step closer to solving your problem, have you?

And everyone has *so* much to say, *so* much that they care about. But I wonder . . . who cares about Becky . . . and who cares about Jan?

SCENE 4 ●
THE TROUBLE WITH JAN

The Town Square

The scene begins in darkness with the **Children** *chanting and clapping. Then a spotlight comes up to reveal* **Jan** *alone in the centre. The other* **Children** *stand in a wide circle around him, in the shadows.*

Throughout the first part of the scene, **Jan** *remains 'frozen' like a statue, not responding in any way to the* **Children's** *comments about him.*

CHILDREN	One potato, two potato, three potato, four, Five potato, six potato, seven potato, more, One, big, *bad* spud behind the kitchen door.
	If you're out in the alley And the lights go out, Here come the Ratz to take you out!
	If you're out in the alley And you feel a clout, Here come the Ratz to take you out!
	If you're out in the alley And you hear a shout, Here come the Ratz to take you out!
JAMES	He's got worse since Becky was taken off.
KEVIN	But he won't talk about it, will he?
PAUL	He's stubborn.
JENNY	Proud.
JO	A loner.
LORNA	And the way he looks at you sometimes, like he's so much better than you, like you belong in the pigsty.
KEVIN	I reckon he uses his foot as an excuse.
PAUL	Yeah. He's always walking round town on his own.
JAMES	It's his own fault he's got no friends.
KEVIN	He should trust people more.
JENNY	The thing that gets me is that little black book he

keeps but never lets anyone look at. Perhaps he's writing about *us*.

As they chant, the **Children** *circle round* **Jan**, *pointing at him, 'counting him out'.*

CHILDREN	Eeny, meeny, macka racka, Dare die, dominacka, Chicka popper, lollypopper, Pig's snout, walk out!
	Eeny, meeny, macka racka, Dare die dominacka, Chicka popper, lollypopper, Pig's snout, walk out!
	Walk out Walk out Walk out Walk out Walk out
	Out Out Out Out OUT!

Blackout

A moment later, a spotlight comes on to reveal the **Stranger** *leaning against a wall, outside the circle of* **Children**. *Another spotlight comes on* **Jan**. *Now it is the* **Children** *who are 'frozen' as the* **Stranger** *and* **Jan** *talk across them.*

STRANGER	*(quietly)* Jan.
JAN	Huh?
STRANGER	Happiest days of your life, aren't they?
JAN	What?
STRANGER	Schooldays.
JAN	No – not for me.
STRANGER	Nor were they for me. But don't worry, I know what it's like. I was always the one who didn't fit in. But it didn't bother me – don't let it bother you. You don't need the likes of *them*. You've got more to offer than them.

JAN	Who are you?
STRANGER	*(softly)* A friend, Jan. Someone who understands.
JAN	You seem to. But . . .
STRANGER	But you don't trust anyone. Don't worry, Jan, I understand.
JAN	Perhaps you do understand.
STRANGER	Yeah, I know what it's like to be alone. After a while you get used to it. Then you get so you don't need other people. That's when you can start to be strong, Jan.
JAN	Where have you come from?
STRANGER	I've been here and there, Jan. Where I'm needed. And right now it's Hamelin.
JAN	I'm glad you're here.
STRANGER	Stick with me, Jan, and I'll show you things beyond your bravest imaginings. Let's see that book.

Pause. Then **Jan** *limps over to the* **Stranger** *and hands him the book.*

JAN	Here.
STRANGER	Hey, these are good, Jan. I like them. Huh, I used to do pictures like this when I was your age. Who's this one?
JAN	That's my Dad. Or at least that's what I think he looked like. But it's so long since he . . .
STRANGER	Now this one I do like. Rows and rows of people in uniform, all without faces. Your classmates?
JAN	You guessed.
STRANGER	I guessed. The same faceless crowd that surrounded me when I was at school. Bo-o-o-o-ring. Oh Jan, you should have seen the kids in my class. All thought I was a weirdo because of the clothes I wore, the way I did my hair. You should see them now – they've never been out of the town we were born in. And me? I've travelled the world: I've dined with emperors and danced with princesses. I've seen more than they could ever dream of. And it could be the same with you, Jan.
JAN	You really think so?

STRANGER	Course I do. You don't need Hamelin. There's more to life than this little town with its little people. You could stay here forever waiting for something to happen to you. Stick with me, Jan, and I'll show you how to make things happen.
JAN	You sound as if . . . as if you really had the power to . . .
STRANGER	That's just it, Jan. Power. Not the power that comes with the Lord Mayor's robes – people like that never change anything, just tinker with what's been handed down to them. Like a drab old suit: take in a bit here, let out a bit there, but never change the style. So long as it's comfy, it'll do. And you never know: one day you might just strike lucky and find an old coin in the lining. No, the real power to change things comes when you can imagine your world *really* different – like in your pictures, Jan – upside down, back to front, inside out. That's when the fun starts.
JAN	Fun?
STRANGER	Fun. Excitement. Fun and games. Not the dreary games of the playground, where everyone has to know their place, be a good sport, stick to the rules and take their turn. All your friends here – they'd never begin to understand the kind of dangerous play we could invent.
JAN	But when I see them together, when they're not ganging up on me, they seem so happy, always smiling and enjoying themselves.
STRANGER	Ah . . . but it's the ones that smile you shouldn't trust, Jan. *(pause)* Have you no friends at all?
JAN	Well – there was Becky. Till she was . . .
STRANGER	Till what? What happened? Tell me, Jan.
JAN	She was taken off by the Ratz. I'll never forget it. We were standing just here. On our own. It was getting dark and the streets were quiet. They came from nowhere and went round so fast. Oh it was horrible. The eyes, the smell, and the screaming . . .

*As **Jan** speaks, the **Ratz** creep out from the shadows, staring at him.*

(*shouting*) And I keep having nightmares. I can't
forget those eyes. I can see them now. Look, look.

The **Stranger** *signals to the advancing* **Ratz**. *They sit down at once,*
gazing up at the **Stranger**.

STRANGER	Oh, the Ratz. Darlings, aren't they? But they do like to play. Don't worry about them.
JAN	You . . . you stopped them. You can control them.
STRANGER	Yes. It's easy when you know how.

With a clap of the hands the **Stranger** *disperses the* **Ratz**.

	But, shhhh. Not a word to anyone. Secret. Between friends, eh? *Friends*, Jan.
JAN	Friends.

SCENE 5 ●
THE BUDGET IS FIXED

The Council Chamber. This is a private Council meeting; no members of the public are present.

Mayor *bangs gavel.*

MAYOR   Fellow Councillors, it is now our duty to discuss the Council budget for next year. As you all know, we have 100,000 guilders at our disposal. We need to agree on priorities for the coming year, but before we open the discussion I would like to remind you all of some important commitments before us. We have the Lord Mayor's Banquet to arrange. And there are other problems as well. There is the Lord Mayor's Procession for which we really are duty bound to purchase an updated carriage. And then there's the matter of the Council Chamber which needs complete refurbishing.

While the **Mayor** *is making this speech,* **Fortune** *sarcastically reinforces each of his priorities for the year.*

FORTUNE   Oh yes . . . *so* important . . . such a serious problem . . . quite . . . of course.

MAYOR   *(to* **Fortune***)* Quiet, please. There is no call for sarcasm in the Council Chamber.

WITHAM   And then there's the problem of the robes.

FITZPATRICK   Yes, my robe is getting very tatty.

FORTUNE   Oh yes, that is *so* important.

MAYOR   Well, I happen to think it's important.

FITZPATRICK   Mine's wearing a bit thin at the shoulders.

WITHAM   Perhaps we could all have new robes.

PHIPP   Definitely. Splendid idea.

FORTUNE   *(defiantly)* I don't want a new robe.

WORTHINGTON   Lord Mayor. Surely Hamelin has one other

	problem that's far more important than these items?
MAYOR	Yes, I agree with you there. We as a Council are facing one major problem this year. I have been there and seen it for myself. I have been to the Council cellars and seen that wine stocks are low. Very low.
FORTUNE	*(sarcastically)* Oh dear. How terrible.
WITHAM	I agree – it's scandalous.
FITZPATRICK	The wine stock is important. We simply can't afford to let this state of affairs continue.
PHIPP	And we will need plenty of wine for the Lord Mayor's Banquet.
WORTHINGTON	Why do we need to have a banquet?
COUNCILLORS	*(all at the same time except* **Fortune** *and* **Worthington**) Don't be ridiculous. Of course we have to hold it. We have the banquet *every* year. It's an important tradition in Hamelin.
FORTUNE	No – why do we need to have a banquet?
MAYOR	We need to have a banquet. It is part of our civic duty to maintain the public dignity of this body, to keep the Council in high esteem.
FORTUNE	You mean to show off . . .
MAYOR	. . . and to reward local dignitaries.
FORTUNE	Like who?
MAYOR	Well . . . like us . . .
FITZPATRICK	Exactly. We are people of some substance.
MAYOR	And . . . er . . . well . . . all my friends.
FORTUNE	Huh!
COUNCILLORS	*(all at the same time)* Stop interrupting. Please. Wait your turn.
GRAHAME	Excuse me, Lord Mayor, may I inquire? When is the Lord Mayor's Banquet?
MAYOR	In three months' time.
WORTHINGTON	I just can't believe this. Surely we've got more important business to discuss?
PHIPP	Like the state of the parks. I would like to put in a bid for some public spending on the town's parks, in particular for restocking the shrubberies and

	repairing all this recent vandalism. Why, only recently three of our attractively carved benches were thrown into the ornamental fountain . . .
FORTUNE	Probably drunkards returning from one of the Lord Mayor's banquets.
WITHAM	How dare you suggest that?
MAYOR	The guests at my banquets are friends of mine not some . . .
FORTUNE	*(shouts)* No they're not . . . they're just people you want to show off to.
MAYOR	They are high-class people, pillars of society – not hooligans.
FITZPATRICK	How dare you suggest that the Lord Mayor mixes with hooligans?
WITHAM	Yes. I demand that you retract that statement.

Long pause. **Fortune** *stands her ground.*

PHIPP	Our parks are a major tourist attraction. I propose that we set aside 10,000 guilders.
WITHAM	Seconded.
MAYOR	We'll put that to the vote then.

At every vote, the result is always the same. **Phipp, Grahame, Witham** *and* **Fitzpatrick** *always vote for the motions,* **Fortune** *and* **Worthington** *always vote against. At first, the* **Mayor** *makes a point of counting votes, but after a while does not even bother to look up as he knows the result is a forgone conclusion.*

	All those in favour? *(four votes)* All those against? *(two votes)* Very well. Motion carried. And now . . . what about the carriage?
GRAHAME	Well, we can hardly use last year's carriage again. What will people think?
WITHAM	Yes. The state of the upholstery is appalling.
FITZPATRICK	And I would like to think that we could put up a really good show this year and get an even better carriage than they have in Hanover.
PHIPP	Hear, hear.
FORTUNE	*(sarcastically)* I know – I've got a really good idea that will solve all our problems. Why don't we

	buy ourselves a new carriage every week?
FITZPATRICK	Don't be ridiculous. Absolutely absurd.
WITHAM	No, that's a bit too much. Just every year.
MAYOR	Once a week would be too expensive. Surely?
FORTUNE	Joke. It . . . was . . . a . . . joke.
WORTHINGTON	How many carriages do we have for goodness sake? Have you been down there to see how many we already have?
WITHAM	Yes. And it's very nice.
GRAHAME	We use them all in the procession. You know we do.
FORTUNE	*(furious)* How many carriages do we need? How many Lord Mayors do we have? I'll tell you. We don't have a Lord Mayor at all, because this one hasn't got the guts to address himself to the *real* problems in Hamelin.
MAYOR	So how much should we set aside for a new carriage?
WITHAM	At least 40,000 guilders.
GRAHAME	Perhaps we should buy ourselves a cheaper carriage.
FITZPATRICK	You get what you pay for with carriages.
PHIPP	The people of Hamelin deserve the very best. I propose 50,000 guilders.
WITHAM	Seconded.
PHIPP	We all know how much the people love the Lord Mayor's Procession, and how much they love to see him wave from a smart new carriage.

The **Mayor** *is in a reverie, waving to the crowd from an imaginary carriage. The others all stare at him and he wakes up with a start.*

MAYOR	Quite, quite.
	Now, all those in favour? *(four votes)*
	All those against? *(two votes)*
	Carried.
WORTHINGTON	Waste of money. What about the Ratz?
WITHAM	What about the wine stocks?
WORTHINGTON	Waste of public money.
FITZPATRICK	How much can we afford to set aside for restocking our cellars? 10,000? 20,000?

FORTUNE	Lord Mayor. We are constantly warning the public against the dangers of drinking too much, yet here we are with our drunken banquets advertising alcoholism.
MAYOR	As I said earlier, the people I invite are . . . well . . . high class.
FORTUNE	Like yourself?
MAYOR	They are not liable to get drunk at civic functions.
FORTUNE	Well, what about what happened at last year's Lord Mayor's Banquet? 33 windows smashed in the Town Hall. How do you explain that?
MAYOR	That was just high spirits.
WITHAM	Quite. Now what about the wine stocks? *If* Ms Fortune will let us get on with our business.
FITZPATRICK	And we must not forget the champagne.
WORTHINGTON	Have we forgotten the Ratz?
FORTUNE	Yes. What about the Ratz?
WITHAM	We're on the subject of wine now.
COUNCILLORS	*(all at the same time)* Yes. Be quiet. Follow the correct procedure. Wait your turn.
GRAHAME	Well, may I propose that we spend 10,000 guilders on restocking the wine cellars?
PHIPP	I'll second that.
WITHAM	My brother-in-law is a wine merchant. I'm sure he would be prepared to assist the Council in this important civic matter.
MAYOR	Thank you, Councillor Witham. All those in favour? *(four votes)* All those against? *(two votes)* Motion carried.
FORTUNE	*(now very angry)* What about the Ratz? It's our responsibility.
MAYOR	How can you possibly say it's our responsibility?
FORTUNE	Of course it is. For years we've had the chance to do something about the East Side, and it's still a slum area. We had the chance last year to do something about the Ratz, but we ignored it. It's the same this year. You'd rather buy new carriages, new robes, new wines. You're always

	ignoring the problem, but it won't go away you know.
WORTHINGTON	Lord Mayor, I would just like to say that the fact that a child has been taken away by the Ratz, kidnapped in *our* town, is far more important than wine cellars, and I feel sure that a lot of people in this town would agree with me.
MAYOR	That's a matter for the police.
WORTHINGTON	But we haven't got enough police.
PHIPP	Perhaps we should spend more on the police force.
FITZPATRICK	The army more like. That's the way to get rid of them.
WITHAM	Hear, hear.
FORTUNE	Quite honestly, I feel sorry for my fellow Councillors when I hear them expressing these ridiculous attitudes. We're talking about fellow creatures.
MAYOR	Are you by any chance referring to the Ratz?
FORTUNE	Yes!
MAYOR	But they're criminals.
FORTUNE	And we're criminals for ignoring the problem!
WORTHINGTON	The Ratz have feelings, you know.

Uproar in the Council Chamber, all the others shouting at **Fortune** *and* **Worthington**.

MAYOR	Order! Order, please. Do we have any further proposals?
WITHAM	Yes. We need a public redecoration programme. The Council Chamber needs refurbishing.
FITZPATRICK	Quite. Just look at the state of it.
PHIPP	New curtains.
GRAHAME	10,000 guilders?
WITHAM	Seconded.
MAYOR	All those in favour? *(four votes)* All those against? *(two votes)* Carried.
FORTUNE	*(shouts)* What are we going to do about the Ratz?
MAYOR	There are other things more important than the Ratz.

FORTUNE	No there aren't! You just want to forget about them! Just because you've at last become Mayor like your father and his father before him, all you want is a smooth year in office with everything plain sailing for you. Well I'll tell you now, if I have anything to do with it, it won't be plain sailing for you.
WITHAM	That sounds like a threat.
FORTUNE	It was!

Councillors *react furiously.*

MAYOR	Order in Council, please. Really, you're worse than that rabble at last night's public meeting. Now, are we agreed on our budget? Carriage, wine, parks, Council Chamber?
WORTHINGTON	What about the Ratz?
GRAHAME	Lord Mayor, may I make a suggestion? We have a small amount left in this year's budget. Give that to the police, so at least we can be seen to be doing something. After all, the public do want us to do something.
PHIPP	Yes, but not too much. Remember my shrubs.
GRAHAME	Then we could make the Ratz a priority for next year's budget.
WITHAM	I agree. We could set up a special committee to discuss the Ratz – next year!
MAYOR	Well that looks like everything's settled then, and I have to say I think we've done Hamelin proud. And I'm sure a little problem like the Ratz would best be dealt with by a special committee.

The **Councillors** *leave. Spotlight comes up to reveal the* **Stranger** *in the middle of the Council Chamber.*

STRANGER	So . . . the Ratz will wait till next year, will they? I wonder. Let's see what they think.

The **Stranger** *raises his arms. Three slow chords as he lowers them and summons the* **Ratz** *who rush into the Chamber from all directions.*

SCENE 6 ●
RATZ IN THE CHAMBER

Ratmusic. Lights. Strobe.

The **Ratz** *charge through the Chamber, over the furniture etc. The* **Stranger** *signals to the* **Ratz** *and they stop. They stare at the Chamber in quiet awe, making occasional sounds to show that they have never seen anything like this before.*

| RAT 2 | *Hey. Look at this. This is where the Mayor sits.* |
| RATZ | *Oh yeah. Look at that.* |

Rat 1 *whistles loudly from the other end of the room. He has found and put on the Mayor's robe and is prancing around in it.*

| RAT 1 | *Oy. Look at me. I'm the Mayor.* |

Laughter, wolf-whistles, jeers etc. from the other **Ratz.** **Rat 2** *makes a* [*fanfare noise. The other* **Ratz** *join in, forming a guard of honour for the 'Mayor'.* **Rat 1** *proceeds regally down the line. The* **Ratz** *bow and scrape,* [*kiss the 'Mayor's' hand, pretend to wave flags etc.*

Rat 1 *orders a* **Rat** *to kiss his foot. The* **Rat** *mimes gratitude, and kisses the foot with mock relish.* **Rat 1** *continues his progress down the line until* **Rat 2** *blows a loud raspberry.*

All the **Ratz** *laugh and immediately disperse round the room.*

Rat 1 *finds the gavel and slams it down. Instantly the* **Ratz** *go into a mime of the Council in session. They take up places on the Council floor and bleat and blah at one another.*

A sneeze is heard.

The **Ratz** *freeze in horror, staring and pointing at the place from which the noise came. They push* **Rat 3** *forward, forcing him/her to investigate.* **Rat 3** *discovers* **Jan** *who has been hiding in the Chamber. He looks frightened. The* **Ratz** *relax, relieved.*

| RATZ | *Oh, that's all it was.* |
| RAT 3 | *Don't worry, mate. We won't hurt you. Urggh. Your leg. Horrible.* |

RATZ   (quietly) **Horrible.**

The **Ratz** *recoil in disgust, hissing. All except for* **Becky**, *now a Rat too. Not only is she dressed and made up like the others but she now also speaks only 'Ratspeak'.* **Becky** *goes up to* **Jan** *and he recognises her.*

JAN   Becky! You . . . you're . . . you're a Rat!
BECKY   **Yeah!**

Becky *gives* **Jan** *a friendly, playful cuff, then picks up the litter bin and sprinkles some of its contents over* **Jan's** *head before throwing more rubbish at other* **Ratz**, *shouting* **Yah** *every time she chucks a piece at one of them.* **Becky** *then pulls* **Rat 4** *over to* **Jan** *and tells him to look at* **Jan's** *leg.*

BECKY   **See. It's a real leg.**
RAT 4   *(to the* **Ratz***)* **It is a real leg. It's all right.**
                   (to **Jan***)* **Go on, mate. Walk. Show them.**

Jan *starts to walk.* **Rat 8** *rushes up to* **Jan** *and grabs the black book out of his hand. S/he opens the book and shouts excitedly to the other* **Ratz**.

RAT 8   **Look at these!**
RAT 9   **Like great graffiti.   Yeah!**

Ratz 8 *and* **9** *gather round* **Jan** *and mime aerosoling with hissing noises. As they do this, they pat him on the back and point excitedly to the pages in the book. The other* **Ratz** *applaud.*

Becky *puts her arm round* **Jan** *and the* **Stranger** *walks the other side of him. The* **Ratz** *follow on and turn it into a procession, chanting* **Oy . . . oy . . . oy . . . oy** *as they go.*

The **Stranger** *leads* **Jan** *up to the Mayor's seat, then signals to the* **Ratz** *to stay where they were before as 'Councillors'. The* **Ratz** *watch in awe as the* **Stranger** *puts the Mayor's robe on* **Jan** *and then places the chain of office round his neck. The* **Ratz** *cheer wildly:* **Oy . . . oy . . . oy . . . oy . . .**

Now the **Ratz** *break into another disorderly Council meeting, shouting, bleating, blahing, throwing paper missiles etc.* **Jan** *looks frightened.*

STRANGER   *(hands* **Jan** *the gavel)* Jan. Try this.

Jan *bangs the gavel nervously. Instantly, the* **Ratz** *are silent and still. Then all the* **Ratz** *start shouting demands at* **Jan** *all at the same time. Uproar.* **Jan** *bangs the gavel and gets them quiet before speaking.*

29

JAN	*(unsure)* What are you doing? What do you want? I don't know what you want.
BECKY	**We want somewhere decent to live.**
RATZ	**Yeah. Yeah. That's what we want.**

Stranger *raises his hand and the* **Ratz** *are silenced.*

STRANGER	Jan. Just listen to the Ratz and you will find out what they want.
BECKY	**We want somewhere decent to live.**
JAN	You mean you want somewhere decent to live?
RATZ	**Yeah. That's what we want.**
JAN	A big house?
RATZ	*(cheering, whistling etc.)* **Yeah.**
STRANGER	Let's make that official now, Jan. Go on.
JAN	*(nervously)* Er . . . I hereby propose that all the Ratz be given the best houses in Hamelin to live in.

Ratz *cheer, whistle, whoop etc.*

JAN	Including the Mayor's house. (**Ratz** *cheer.*) What else do you want?

Ratz *all shout at the same time, arguing with each other. Uproar.*

STRANGER	It's no good asking *them*. Like everyone else in this town, they can't make up their minds on anything. *Tell* them, Jan.
JAN	No schools. (**Ratz** *cheer wildly.*) No rules.

Ratz *cheer.*

STRANGER	Come on, Jan. Make it official. You'll never forget today. This was the day when you were ruler of all Hamelin. King for a day!
JAN	Er . . . I hereby declare that from now on all rules in Hamelin be abolished. (**Ratz** *cheer.* **Jan** *is wild with excitement now.*) And furthermore, I call upon this august Council (*cheers from* **Ratz**), the chosen representatives of the good burghers of Hamelin (*more cheers from* **Ratz**), to remove all notices, signs, directions from the town.

Ratz *cheer.*

STRANGER	Good, Jan, good. Go to it.
JAN	And the Civic Corporation appoints you . . . you . . . and you to be responsible for Refuse Disposal.
RATZ 5, 6, 7	*Eh?*
JAN	Yes. See you dispose a lot more refuse around this town. It's far too tidy!

Ratz 5, 6 *and* **7** *charge around the room throwing papers etc. up in the air, to the delight of the other* **Ratz.**

STRANGER	That's the stuff, Jan.
JAN	And as for the state of the graffiti in this town. It's terrible.
RATZ	*Eh?*
JAN	Yes, terrible. There's nothing like enough of it. See that every wall we have is sprayed with paint. I hereby appoint you . . . and you to be the official decorators of Hamelin. *(***Ratz 8** *and* **9** *run around as if aerosoling the walls of the Chamber.)* And we'll make all Hamelin our playground.

Ratz *cheer wildly.*

STRANGER	That's the way, Jan. Now you've got them eating out of your hand.
JAN	*(quite carried away now)* And we'll have no books. *(cheers from* **Ratz***)* And no learning. *(more cheers from* **Ratz***)* And no law. *(***Ratz** *cheer.)* And no order. *(more cheers from* **Ratz***)* And in return you'll let me have Becky back.

As soon as **Jan** *says that, the heady atmosphere is broken. The* **Ratz** *boo, hiss and scatter to the faint sounds of distant Ratmusic. Then there is silence.*

STRANGER	Shame, Jan. You had them just where you wanted them – and then you blew it. You've still got a lot to learn – like everyone else in this foolish little town. *(now addressing the audience)* And wasn't it entertaining to see our friends playing at the business of government?

A fine show, I must say. At least it made a pleasant change to see our Council come to a decision! Ratz playing at Council; Councillors playing at Council. Close your eyes and which is which? Soon no-one will neither know nor care, because they'll all be dancing to my tune.

Blackout

SCENE 7 ●
READ ALL ABOUT IT

The Town Square. In the distance, a child's voice can be heard.

CHILD   Read all about it! Read all about it!

Soon all the **Children** *have entered the Square and are shouting out headlines from the newspapers they are handing out.*

CHILDREN   Read all about it! Read all about it!
Ratz Storm Council Chamber!
Ratz On The Rampage!
Ratz In The Chamber!

The **Children** *distribute papers to the* **Citizens** *in the audience but also to the real members of the audience. The* **Citizens** *discuss the shocking news with each other and members of the real audience.*

SPARKS   Well, I think it's about time we did something about this.

BIND   Yeah, so do I.

SPARKS   Listen to me everyone.

BIND   Yeah, listen to him.

They wait till they have established silence from the **Citizens** *and the real audience.*

SPARKS   Right. I've got this petition here and I want you all to sign it. It demands some action from this so-called Council of ours. So far, the Mayor, the Council and the police have done nothing. So it looks like we are going to have to make the first move. I want all of you to sign this petition, and then we'll have some proof that the people in this town want something done about the Ratz.

1st *and* **2nd Citizens** *take copies of the petition through the audience asking everyone to sign.*

3rd CITIZEN	Wait on, Ron.
4th CITIZEN	We'll sign it.

They come out of the audience to join **Sparks** *in the Square.*

3rd CITIZEN	About time someone did something to get that lot on the Council up off their backsides. Give us a pen, then.

They sign. Now other **Citizens** *come into the Square to join in the discussion.*

STRIDE	Mind you, I always said something like this was going to happen sooner or later.
1st CITIZEN	It's an outrage. This town is being overrun.
3rd CITIZEN	It's not safe to go out at night now.
4th CITIZEN	You can't let your kids play out any more.
5th CITIZEN	If you ask me they've gone too far this time.
6th CITIZEN	Why the hell don't the police do something about it?
1st CITIZEN	The police? In Hamelin? Huh. That's a joke.
2nd CITIZEN	Well, I reckon it serves the Council right. About time the Ratz did something to *them*. Maybe now they'll realise what life is really like in this town.
1st CITIZEN	You've got a point there.
5th CITIZEN	Maybe this petition thingy will help too.
6th CITIZEN	The Council never listens to anything we say.
7th CITIZEN	Exactly. So what's the point? I'll tell you one thing for certain – I won't be wasting my time signing that petition.
WRIGHT	No. Wait. Let me ask you a question.
7th CITIZEN	Huh?
WRIGHT	Who's going to pay for all this damage to their precious Council Chamber?
7th CITIZEN	Well . . . the Council, I suppose.
WRIGHT	Yes, but who pays for the Council? I'll tell you – we're all going to pay for it. Me, you . . . and you . . . and you . . . yes, every single one of us. We're *all* going to pay for this.

Blackout

34

SCENE 8 ●
TRAPS FOR RATZ

The Town Square

TOWNCRIER   Oyez . . . oyez . . . oyez . . . on behalf of the
Hamelin Town Council, an important public
announcement.

Following the disgraceful goings on in the
Council Chamber last night, the Lord Mayor
hereby announces that a reward of 20,000 – yes,
20,000 – guilders will be granted to any citizen of
Hamelin who can devise a scheme, machine or
trap to catch the Ratz. Anyone wishing to claim
this reward must first qualify as a citizen of this
town. Furthermore, in the interests of public
safety, all devices or traps must be examined and
approved by the Council prior to being left out on
the streets. The Council wishes well to anyone
intending to enter this competition and to work
towards a Rat-free Hamelin.

Blackout

The lights come up to reveal all the **Councillors** *with the* **Towncrier**.
Some **Citizens** *are present, some remain in audience.*

TOWNCRIER   And now . . . may we please have the first
machine?

Enter three **Inventors** *with a 'trap'. It is a hardboard 'wall', which comes
in three hinged sections, with a long piece of cord attached to one end.
Bricks are painted on the 'wall' and the whole trap is taller than a person.*

Throughout the demonstration of the machine, the **Citizens** *in the
audience react with applause, scepticism, or even questions.*

1st INVENTOR Ladies and gentlemen, this simple but effective
rat trap is based on this section of brick wall. But
here we have to let you into a little secret.

2nd INVENTOR   It isn't a real wall!

1st INVENTOR   Quite. The wall here is the bait. Now as you all know, Ratz love to spray graffiti on walls. No self-respecting Rat will ever be able to resist this bit of fresh, unspoilt wall. Perhaps we could have a volunteer at this stage?

The **Inventors** *choose a volunteer from the audience – ideally, a genuine spectator, not a 'plant'. They stand the volunteer in front of the wall.* **2nd** *and* **3rd Inventors** *now hide behind each of the outside sections of the wall.*

1st INVENTOR   *(ad libbing with the volunteer)* Now sir/madam, please could you pretend to be one of the Ratz as you approach this wall? That's very good . . . a touch more menace if that's possible . . . Pretend you've got an aerosol in your hand . . . that's it . . . go right up to the wall . . . lovely . . .

Now ladies and gentlemen, while our Rat is spraying the wall my two assistants hidden inside will bring round the sides . . .

The **2nd** *and* **3rd Inventors** *bring round the outside sections to meet at the front, with the volunteer now trapped inside the prism.*

1st INVENTOR   . . . and . . .

2nd INVENTOR   Hey presto! The Rat is trapped.

1st INVENTOR   Then it is simply a matter of . . .

3rd INVENTOR   . . . tying the trap up . . .

They wind cord around the prism and tie a big bow at the front.

2nd INVENTOR   . . . and calling the police.

3rd INVENTOR   Simple, cheap and efficient!

The **Inventors** *untie the cord and release the volunteer.*

MAYOR   Very good. We're all most impressed. I'm sure this machine deserves a round of applause.

The **Mayor** *leads the* **Councillors**, **Citizens** *and audience in applauding.*

1st INVENTOR	Mayor and Councillors, the people of Hamelin need fear the Ratz no more.
MAYOR	Splendid! Splendid! *(to* **Towncrier***)* Well, go on.
TOWNCRIER	What?
MAYOR	The curfew.
TOWNCRIER	Oh yeah. *(clears throat and makes a public announcement)* This ingenious machine will be placed in the Town Square this very night. So, in the interest of public safety, the Lord Mayor announces a curfew to take effect immediately. *(aggressively)* That means now. Would you please return to your homes at once?

Mayor, Councillors, Citizens leave. *The machine is left in place by the* **Inventors.** **1st** *and* **2nd Inventors** *hide behind their wall. Lights fade. Enter the* **Stranger.**

STRANGER	So . . . your Council has finally decided to act on your behalf, now that their sacred Chamber has been damaged. A reward of 20,000 guilders too. Twenty thousand guilders – the price they have set on your safety. And this delightful machine – so ingenious, so resourceful. How thoughtful of the Council to provide the Ratz with such an interesting toy.

The **Stranger** *raises his arms. Same three chords.* **Ratz** *rush in. Ratmusic, lights, strobe etc.*

SCENE 9 ●
SPRINGING THE TRAP

The Town Square. Nightfall.

*The **Stranger** stands by and watches with detached amusement as the **Ratz** rush through the Square and round the machine. When the music, lights etc. fade out, the **Ratz** stop and stare suspiciously at the machine. They approach the wall tentatively. Eventually **Rat 1** taps it. It sounds hollow.*

RAT 2   *Here. Give us a lift up.*

*Other **Ratz** lift him/her up so **Rat 2** can peer over the top of the wall.*

RAT 2   *Oy. There's two idiots behind here.*

*Ratz laugh and cheer. **Rat 3** whistles and calls the others over to the far side of the Square.*

RAT 3   *Here. I've got an idea. Shhh.*

*Ratz all huddle round. Whispers. All the **Ratz** hug themselves in delight, whoop, cheer etc. once they have heard the plan. **Rat 3** shushes them. Silence.*

*Rat 3 tiptoes across to the wall and silently picks up the cord at one end of it. Other **Ratz** go up to the audience on tiptoe and shush them.*

*Rat 3 signals to **Ratz 4** and **5** to help. They fold the wall round the opposite way thus trapping the two **Inventors** inside. The **Inventors** shout in protest as **Rat 3** ties an elaborate knot. All the other **Ratz** celebrate, chanting **Oy . . . oy . . . oy** etc. as the wall rattles and wobbles.*

*Spotlight on the **Stranger** who has been watching everything, but doing nothing.*

STRANGER   All this public entertainment – and it didn't cost the Council anything at all. Catching Ratz isn't quite so simple as they thought. How much easier it would be to catch a pack of Councillors.

Blackout

SCENE 10 ●
FRIENDS TOGETHER

The Town Square. Empty. Silence.

Sounds of **Children** *approaching. They are making car noises, tyre screeching etc. They stop beside the graffiti wall trap.*

LORNA	Will you look at the state of that!
JO	What a tip!
JAMES	Not much of a rat-catching machine, was it?
PAUL	Looks more like a heap of junk.
JENNY	Talk about tinny!
KATE	Our neighbour helped make that! He was really proud of it. It's pathetic.
JAMES	So much for the great inventors of Hamelin.
PAUL	What beats me is how any of them could've been so stupid as to think those machines could ever catch the Ratz.
KEVIN	Your Dad made one didn't he?
PAUL	No way!
JENNY	Yes he did.
PAUL	Well, maybe he helped out a bit, that's all.
KATE	Grown-ups believe in machines.

The **Children** *laugh knowingly.*

JAMES	I'll tell you what I reckon. The Mayor probably knew they wouldn't work. That's why he was prepared to offer such a big reward.
LORNA	20,000 guilders, wasn't it?
KATE	They're stingy on the Council.
JENNY	And the inventors only did it for the money.
JO	They must think the Ratz are dumb.
JAMES	They're not though. It's obvious.
PAUL	Smarter than the Council.

Enter **Jan**. *The* **Children** *ignore him even when he stands near them.*

KEVIN	Mind you. Someone's got to get rid of the Ratz. They're ruining everything round here.
LORNA	You can say that again, Kevin. I'm not allowed out after school. *Ever.*
JO	Me neither.
PAUL	Yeah . . . my mum's really strict about that too.
JENNY	And have you seen what they've done to the swings and slides up at at the rec?
JAN	*(quietly)* I know someone who can get rid of the Ratz.
JAMES	And now the swimming pool's shut because of the damage.
JAN	I know someone who can get rid of the Ratz.
CHILDREN	*(together)* Sure thing, Jan. Oh yeah. Like heck you do.
JAN	No. Really. I know someone who can control the Ratz.
JENNY	All right, then. Who?
JAN	I . . . don't know who he is.

The **Children** *all laugh at* **Jan**.

LORNA	Sure, Jan. Because he doesn't exist.
JAMES	No, give him a chance. Come on then, Jan. Tell us who it is.
JAN	I told you. I don't know who it was. I'd never seen him . . . it . . . before.
JENNY	What's his name?
JAN	He . . . she didn't say.
PAUL	What do you mean 'he . . . she'? Is it a boy or a girl?
JAN	It's hard to tell. At least I'm not sure.

The **Children** *all gather round* **Jan**.

JO	What does . . . he look like?
JAN	Kind of weird.

The **Children** *laugh.*

KATE	Where does . . . it . . . come from?
JAN	Didn't say. Not from round here, anyway.
JAMES	Where did you see him? When did you see him?
JAN	I'm not sure. It was all like a dream. So strange. He said he was . . . my friend.
KEVIN	Perhaps it *was* all a dream.
JAN	No. He can control the Ratz.
JENNY	How do you know?
JAN	I saw him.
PAUL	But if you don't know who he is, or where he comes from, how are you ever going to find him again?
JAN	He'll find me.

Enter the **Stranger**. *The* **Children** *look frightened.*

STRANGER	Jan. You seem to have found yourself some friends at last.
JAN	*(sheepishly)* Yes.
STRANGER	Why's that then, Jan?
JAN	I . . . I told them . . . I told them.
STRANGER	What did you tell them, Jan?
JAN	*(ashamed)* I told them you could help us get rid of the Ratz.
STRANGER	Did you, then? *Our* secret, Jan. A secret between friends. *(to* **Children***)* And . . . do you believe him?

The **Children** *back off, nodding awkwardly. Except for* **Kevin**.

STRANGER	*(to* **Kevin***)* And you? Do you believe him?
KEVIN	No way. I think he's just up to his usual tricks again.
STRANGER	Tricks? You want tricks? I'll show you a trick. Ratz!

The **Stranger** *raises his/her arms. Same three chords.* **Ratz** *rush in from every direction and surround the* **Children***. They stop. Silence. Then suddenly all the* **Ratz** *leap forward and scream, frightening the* **Children***. The* **Stranger** *claps his/her hands.* **Ratz** *go silent, looking up* *at the* **Stranger**. *The* **Stranger** *helps* **Jan** *up on to bench.*

STRANGER   There we are, then. Ratz. Ratz for you to play
with. *(The* **Children** *cower in fear.)* We're going
to play a game. And Jan's going to lead it.

JAN   Right we're going to play 'tag'. All the children
are on it and they've got to 'tag' the Ratz. Go on.
Play.

The **Ratz** *scatter round the Square. At first the* **Children** *are nervous,
but soon a wild game of 'tag' is in progress. The* **Ratz** *are brilliant at it.
The game continues until the* **Stranger** *claps hands.*

STRANGER   That's enough. Ratz, scatter! *(The* **Ratz** *leave
instantly.)* Well. Do you believe Jan now? *(The*
Children *all nod.)* Do you believe I can get rid of
the Ratz? *(They nod.)* Do you believe *we* – Jan
and I – can get rid of the Ratz? *(They nod.)* Right.
And there's big money in this, you know. Money
for us – for me, for Jan and for Jan's friends. So
what are we going to do?

LORNA   We'll have to tell the Mayor.

PAUL   We can't do anything by ourselves.

JO   We'll have to go to the Town Hall.

JENNY   They'll never listen to us.

JAMES   They'll have to this time.

JAN   Come on. Let's do it now. Let's go and see the
Council.

Children *gather behind* **Jan** *and march out chanting.*

CHILDREN   We want to see the Council!
We want to see the Council!
We want to see the Council!

The **Stranger** *leaves with them.*

42

SCENE 11 ●
A DEAL IS STRUCK

The Council Chamber

The **Councillors** *are seated behind a table.*

The **Children** *enter, led by* **Jan,** *still chanting,* 'We want to see the Council.' *Many of the* **Citizens** *have joined the march. The* **Stranger** *is with them.*

The **Councillors** *look flustered, astonished, angry and mutter to one another.*

COUNCILLORS *(together)* What's going on?
What are these children doing here?
Who let them in?
Who's that?

The **Stranger** *steps forward and beckons to the* **Children** *and* **Citizens** *to sit down on the floor. They do so.* **Stranger** *remains standing, facing the* **Councillors.**

MAYOR	Your name?
STRANGER	I understand you have a problem.
FORTUNE	And I understand the Lord Mayor asked you a question. Would you please answer it.
STRANGER	I see you have a problem here in Hamelin. A very serious problem.
WITHAM	Yes . . . we do have a problem. So?
STRANGER	Thank you.
WORTHINGTON	What do *you* intend to do about this problem?
STRANGER	I intend to get rid of the Ratz for you.

Reaction from the **Citizens**.

MAYOR	How?
STRANGER	And why should I tell you that? If I was to tell you how to get rid of the Ratz, then you would act upon it yourselves, wouldn't you?

MAYOR	We can't rely on what you've told us. Unless we know what you intend to do, we can't pay you any money.
STRANGER	Money? Who said anything about money? But tell me, Lord Mayor, tell me, Hamelin Town Council: what's it really worth to you?

The **Councillors** *confer.*

FITZPATRICK	Who is he . . . she . . . it?
PHIPP	Not a citizen of Hamelin, that's for sure!
WITHAM	He reminds me of a Rat.
GRAHAME	I see what you mean.
FORTUNE	Well, I'm not happy about giving public moneys to this conman. I've said it enough times, the only way to solve this problem is long-term public investment.
WORTHINGTON	Not on crackpot schemes to get rid of the Ratz.
MAYOR	5,000 guilders?

Fitzpatrick, **Witham**, **Grahame** *and* **Phipp** *all show their assent.*

MAYOR	*(to* **Stranger***)* 5,000 guilders. *If* you get rid of the Ratz.
STRANGER	5,000. And that's what it's worth, is it?
MAYOR	I think it's quite a generous offer.
STRANGER	5,000 guilders. Well, well, well. And yet you are prepared to spend – how much – 10,000 on your parks. And, remind me – how much on redecorating this Council Chamber?
FITZPATRICK	10,000. *(The other* **Councillors** *shush him.)* I mean . . . er . . .
STRANGER	And how much was it on restocking your wine cellars? Another 10,000, wasn't it?

The **Citizens** *are outraged.*

BIND	10,000 guilders on wine!
STRIDE	That's an outrage!
MAYOR	How do you know all this? It's confidential information.
WRIGHT	You're spending our taxes on these things?

STRANGER	And yet you put up a mere 5,000 guilders to get rid of the Ratz? Come, now. And I understand – but do please correct me if I'm wrong – that the Council has ordered a new carriage. To cost – yes, 50,000 guilders.
CITIZENS	*(together)* You what? 50,000 guilders? On a carriage? How much?
MAYOR	This is all lies. The man's an imposter.
SPARKS	Is he?
CALLOW	All right. What is happening to our money then?
1st CITIZEN	Where's it all going to?
WRIGHT	Would you mind clearing this up? For public information. Is this person telling the truth or not?
CROUCH	Have you thought what might happen if the Press were to get hold of this information? Oh dear, I shudder to think.
MAYOR	But he's an imposter.
BIND	Are you buying a new carriage?
MAYOR	Yes . . . we . . . are.
CITIZENS	*(variously)* How much, then? What'll it cost?
WITHAM	That's no concern of yours.
CITIZENS	*(variously)* Yes it is! Of course it is! Tell us!
PARKS	But it is some concern of ours. It's *our* money. I don't see why the Council should spend 50,000 on a new carriage and yet only 5,000 on getting rid of the Ratz.
STRANGER	Perhaps you would like some time to think it over.
FORTUNE	We have nothing to think about, thank you.
STRANGER	I think you have. You've got a lot to think about. Because if you don't Hamelin is going to be left with a serious problem on its hands, with these Ratz. And if you don't do something about it quickly, it will only get worse.

The **Stranger** *leaves. The* **Citizens** *start to berate the* **Councillors**.

CALLOW	Now look what you've done. You've wasted our only chance.
1st CITIZEN	Now he's gone.
2nd CITIZEN	We'll never find out whether or not he can get rid of the Ratz unless you give him a chance.
WRIGHT	If this Council cared, they would be prepared to pay any price he named so long as he got rid of the Ratz.
GRAHAME	But how can we trust him? We don't even know who he is. We at least need some kind of identification before we can talk about prices. Surely?
FITZPATRICK	He's an absolute charlatan. Just look at the way he dresses for a start!
MAYOR	For all we know he could be one of the Ratz.
SPARKS	I reckon he'd do better on the Council than some of you lot.
BIND	How come you're prepared to offer 20,000 guilders to anyone else, yet you'll only offer him 5,000 for the same job?

The other **Citizens** *support him*.

3rd CITIZEN	I think we should go along with him. You never know.
MAYOR	I don't see how this . . . person . . . can expect singlehandedly to solve the whole problem.
CITIZENS	*(variously)* Well, let's see. At least give him a chance. It's worth a try.
4th CITIZEN	This might be our only chance.
STRIDE	We don't know he's a fake. 5,000 isn't enough for the job.
FORTUNE	But we don't even know what his price is. He might ask for much more.
WORTHINGTON	Waste of public money!
WRIGHT	If the Mayor can afford 50,000 guilders on a carriage for his procession, then he can afford at least 10,000 on this.

46

CITIZENS	(variously) More.
	I agree.
	Hear, hear.
	Do a deal with him.
MAYOR	(desperate) All right! All right! We'll listen to you.
CITIZENS	(stunned) Eh?
MAYOR	We'll do a deal with him. We'll do as you suggest. But not a penny over 10,000 guiders.
FORTUNE	But we don't know his price!
GRAHAME	May I suggest that we at least listen to him again?

The **Stranger** *returns, carrying a rolled up piece of paper.*

STRANGER	Well . . . since you can't make up your minds, here are *my* terms. I'll do the job for 1,000 guilders.
ALL	What? 1,000 guilders?
STRANGER	But first I want a contract. I want a contract with the town of Hamelin. Signed by *all* your Councillors.

The **Stranger** *hands the contract to the* **Mayor**.

CITIZENS	(all shouting at once) Sign it . . .
	Cheap . . .
	1,000 guilders . . .
	Go on . . .
MAYOR	Quiet, please! Order! (reads from the contract) 'We, the undersigned Councillors of Hamelin, on behalf of its citizens, hereby agree to pay the sum of 1,000 guilders once he has rid Hamelin of the Ratz.'
PHIPP	Seems reasonable enough.
CITIZENS	(shouting) Just sign it . . . sign it . . .

The **Councillors** *mutter.* **Fortune** *and* **Worthington** *shake their heads and keep saying 'I don't like it . . . It's not right' etc.*

The contract is then signed by each **Councillor** *in turn. As each one signs, they say something.*

FITZPATRICK	1,000 guilders. By Jove, we've hit the jackpot!
WITHAM	Well . . . I'll sign it for a thousand. But I wouldn't for twenty.
PHIPP	This might be our only chance.
MAYOR	Well this person . . . if he can get rid of the Ratz, shall have his 1,000 guilders. But if he doesn't, not a penny.
FORTUNE	This is under protest.
WORTHINGTON	Likewise. I cannot approve of this scheme.
CITIZENS	*(variously)* Look. They've all signed it. At last! *(some clap, cheer)*
MAYOR	*(stands up)* Sir . . . your contract. *(hands the contract to the* **Stranger***)*
STRANGER	Thank you. I believe we have a deal. *(pointing contract at* **Citizens***)* We have a deal. *(to audience)* We have a deal.

Blackout

SCENE 12 ●
TAKING OFF THE RATZ

Town Square. Middle of the night.

*The **Stranger** walks slowly to the centre, raises arms. Same three chords. The **Ratz** come in quietly, hissing.*

*The **Stranger** puts a finger to his lips, silences the **Ratz**, then gestures for them to crouch down in a circle around him.*

*The **Stranger** walks a few paces away. He beckons to the **Ratz** and they follow him, silently, in a tight pack. All the **Ratz** stare at the **Stranger** as if mesmerised. Teasing, he walks slowly, occasionally spinning round and signalling to the **Ratz** to stop in their tracks and crouch down. As they proceed round the Square, they resemble a game of Grandmother's Footsteps played at speed, silently and with menace.*

*Suddenly the **Stranger** quickens the pace of this macabre game. He stands at the centre and fans the **Ratz** around him in a wide circle. He conducts them as they circle him faster and faster. The **Ratz**' eyes are fixed on the **Stranger**. They are completely in his power. At a whim, the **Stranger** stops the circle and then spins the **Ratz** round in the opposite direction.*

*Arms aloft, the **Stranger** speeds up the pace again. Then without any notice he diverts the stream of **Ratz** out of the Square. They rush out. The **Stranger** looks around, shrugs his shoulders and saunters off.*

Blackout

SCENE 13 ●
A BREACH OF CONTRACT

The Council Chamber. Councillors' meeting.

MAYOR Well, what of these rumours, then? Do you really think one . . . person . . . could singlehandedly have removed *all* the Ratz from the town?

WORTHINGTON If he has, we are going to have to pay him.

FITZPATRICK But how do we know if the Ratz are gone, just because the streets are quiet today? The Ratz often keep out of the centre of town for a week at a time. We need to know for sure.

PHIPP Perhaps they are in hiding.

FORTUNE We need some hard proof. We need to inspect the East Side before we pay out public money to a perfect stranger.

GRAHAME And for that we need time.

WITHAM Well. The document never stated *when* we had to pay him, did it?

GRAHAME I propose that we pay him 100 guilders now. And then, when we know for certain that the Ratz have gone, we can pay him the rest.

WITHAM That's an absurd suggestion! Until we know he's done the job, we shouldn't part with a penny. We just need to delay payment.

MAYOR We could tell him that we can't get the money out of the bank without a few days' notice. That would buy us some time.

WORTHINGTON We can't play that sort of game. The people of this town saw us sign the document. They will expect us to pay him if the Ratz are gone.

FORTUNE Just pay him off and get rid of him quick, I say.

FITZPATRICK Excuse me, Councillor Fortune, but that contract is worth nothing. We signed it, but he didn't. It is therefore not legally binding.

WORTHINGTON But there are witnesses!

PHIPP	It's not dated.
GRAHAME	It doesn't even give his name.
WITHAM	Then it's not a legal contract! We've got him there!
FITZPATRICK	Not worth the paper it's written on!
FORTUNE	That's not the point. And if he has got rid of the Ratz and we don't pay him, what if he then brings them all back into the town?
WITHAM	That would be blackmail! Protection money!
MAYOR	Quite. Councillor Fortune, you of all people cannot seriously be suggesting that we use public money for some sort of protection racket? *(Embarrassed silence. After a while,* **Grahame** *raises her hand.)* Councillor Grahame?
GRAHAME	Lord Mayor. If he has got rid of the Ratz and if he has . . . well . . . killed them, where does that put us?

Pause

PHIPP	In prison, that's where.
FORTUNE	We would be accessories to the crime. Our signatures are on that document.
FITZPATRICK	There's no doubt about it. We've got to get that document back somehow.
WORTHINGTON	But what about all those witnesses?
MAYOR	They were the ones who wanted us to sign it. They're in this as deep as we are. They put pressure on us. And anyway, we signed it on their behalf. *We* can't be held responsible. *(pause)* And now, do we have any proposals? How about Mrs Grahame's suggestion?
GRAHAME	I propose we pay him 100 now. And then, when we have established that he's got rid of the Ratz, we pay him the remaining 900.
FORTUNE	Hear, hear. I second that.
MAYOR	Any counter proposals?
WITHAM	Yes. I propose that we don't pay him anything until we are certain that he has got rid of the Ratz.
FITZPATRICK	Seconded.

MAYOR	Well, which is it to be?
FORTUNE	Put it to the vote.
MAYOR	Right. All those in favour of Mrs Grahame's idea?

Fortune, Worthington *and* **Grahame** *all vote.*

And all those in favour of Mr Witham's?

Witham, Fitzpatrick *and* **Phipp** *all vote.* **Mayor** *gives casting vote for this proposal.*

	Well, that's it.
FORTUNE	We're making excuses. Excuses, excuses, it's the story of our lives.
WORTHINGTON	We've got to face up to the problem.

The **Stranger** *enters.*

STRANGER	I have come for my money.
MAYOR	What's this?
STRANGER	I have completed the work you required of me. And now I want my payment.
WORTHINGTON	Of course we will pay you, once we know for certain that you have done the job.
STRANGER	You have my word.
MAYOR	Oh, come. We will need more than that!
FITZPATRICK	Do you have any witnesses?
WITHAM	Do you have any proof?
STRANGER	You have my word. I trusted *you*.
FORTUNE	But you must understand, we do need some time to see that the Ratz really have gone.
MAYOR	And besides, we need time to get the money out of the bank.
STRANGER	You promised me. You signed this contract.
MAYOR	That's a matter for our legal department. You'll have to leave it with them.
WITHAM	And in any case, we don't believe that it is a legally binding contract between two parties. One party, yourself, is not even mentioned in the contract. You have not signed it.

PHIPP	And it doesn't say *when* we have to pay you.
STRANGER	But it does have *your* signatures upon it. You all signed it.
FITZPATRICK	Would you mind if I had a look?
STRANGER	Of course not. See.

Fitzpatrick crosses over to the **Stranger** *who shows him the contract. Suddenly* **Fitzpatrick** *makes a grab for the contract, but the* **Stranger** *coolly whips it out of his reach and motions to him to go back to his place.* **Fitzpatrick** *returns, looking embarrassed.*

	Oh dear. And you were all so keen to sign it.
GRAHAME	May I ask you – how did you dispose of the Ratz?
STRANGER	*(harshly)* What's that to you? All you asked was that I got rid of them.
FORTUNE	Was it in a humane way?
WORTHINGTON	We hope you haven't injured or killed any?
STRANGER	You weren't so bothered about that before. Why all this sudden concern now that it's time for you to make *your* side of the bargain? *(unrolls the contract and scrutinises it)* Well, let's see what the contract says. I can see nothing about being humane, not injuring, not killing. It's not here, I'm sorry. It doesn't say *how* I should do the job.
FITZPATRICK	No. But nor does it say *when* we have to pay you. Does it?
PHIPP	It's not a proper contract. We don't have to pay you.
GRAHAME	How can we pay you? We don't even know who you are.
STRANGER	You asked me to get rid of them. I did that. Now I want my money.
MAYOR	Yes, but do we have any proof?
STRANGER	You have my word.
MAYOR	Your word is not enough, I'm afraid. We need proof.
STRANGER	*(firmly)* I trusted you. For the last time, will you pay me?
MAYOR	Not yet. We need time.
STRANGER	And I have run out of time. I had a deal with the town of Hamelin. I kept my part of the bargain,

but you failed to keep yours. So . . . it looks as if my work in Hamelin is not yet finished.

The **Stranger** *turns on his heels and walks out purposefully.*

SCENE 14 ●
SETTLING THE SCORE

The Town Square

Kevin *and* **Jo** *rush in breathless, searching round desperately for somewhere to hide.*

In the distance can be heard a blood-curdling chant, approaching rapidly.
'RAT ATTACK -A-RAT-A-TAT-ATTACK!
RAT ATTACK -A-RAT-A-TAT-ATTACK!'

Kevin *and* **Jo** *can find no hiding place, as the sounds are approaching from all sides of the Square.*

The **Children** *burst in, still chanting. They isolate* **Kevin** *and encircle him.* **James** *leaps at him and 'claws'* **Kevin**.

JAMES   Gotcha!

Kevin *now joins the others as they approach* **Jo** *and encircle her. As they circle round her, they chant, almost in a whisper now.*

CHILDREN   RAT ATTACK –A–RAT–A–TAT–ATTACK!
                    RAT ATTACK –A–RAT–A–TAT–ATTACK!

Kevin *now 'tags'* **Jo**.

KEVIN   Rat!

Now all the **Children** *march round together, chanting.*

CHILDREN   RAT ATTACK –A–RAT–A–TAT–ATTACK!
                    RAT ATTACK –A–RAT–A–TAT–ATTACK!

Enter **Jan**. *He urgently tries to get the* **Children's** *attention and is limping as quickly as he can.*

JAN   Listen, everyone, listen!

At first the **Children** *go on chanting and even move in on him, but* **Jan's** *urgency wins through. They go quiet.*

JAN	Listen. It's important.
PAUL	What is it?
JAN	He's done it! I've seen him! I tell you, he's really done it!
JO	What?
KATE	You mean . . .
JAN	Yes. I tell you – he's really done it!
KEVIN	You mean your friend?
JAN	Yes! *My* friend. He's got rid of the Ratz.
JAMES	How do you know?
JAN	He told me. I've just seen him. Just now.
LORNA	But how can you be sure?
JAMES	Yeah . . . just 'cos he says he has, doesn't mean anything.
JO	How do you know he's telling the truth?
JENNY	How do we know you're telling the truth?
JAN	Look. You've got to believe me. You saw him with the Ratz before. You know he can control them. And now he's going to claim his reward.
KATE	The reward?
JAN	Yes. The 1,000 guilders the Council promised him.
JENNY	The 1,000 guilders he promised us.
PAUL	When did you see him, Jan?
JAN	Just now. He was on his way to the Town Hall. He was in a hurry. Said he had to leave town today. But he said that before he went he'd make sure he brought us the reward.
PAUL	1,000 guilders. That's a lot of dosh.
JAMES	Yeah. Think what you could get for that. I'd get [myself some new clothes and a bike for a start.
LORNA	An electronic keyboard.
JO	Rollerboots.
KEVIN	A Walkman. *(pause)* How about you, Jan? What'd you buy?
JAN	I . . . er . . . can't really think of anything much that I want to buy. I'm not sure what I really want.

Enter the **Stranger**.

STRANGER	That's the problem, isn't it, Jan? Knowing what you *really* want. Perhaps it's friends. But you

	certainly seem to have plenty of those now. *(to the* **Children***)* Doesn't he? You're all Jan's friends now, aren't you? *(The* **Children** *nod and mumble, embarrassed.)* And why do you all want to be Jan's friends?
KEVIN	Because he . . . you . . . well, you've got rid of the Ratz.
STRANGER	And?
PAUL	Well . . . the reward too.
STRANGER	Oh yes, the reward. I'd nearly forgotten that. Well, I've just got back from the Council to share with you all that they paid me.

The **Stranger** *takes a pullstring purse out from his belt. The* **Children** *gather round greedily.* **Jan** *holds back. The* **Stranger** *motions to the* **Children** *to sit. They kneel around him, hands outstretched. The* **Stranger** *waves the purse above their outstretched hands, teasing them. Eventually he opens it and shakes out scraps of paper which flutter to the ground. The* **Children** *grab.*

JENNY	Hey, this isn't money.
LORNA	Just scraps of paper.
JO	With writing on.
KATE	You've cheated us.
JENNY	Yeah. We've been cheated.
JAMES	*(turns and squares up to* **Jan***)* I suppose you planned all this, Jan.
JENNY	Yeah. I bet you never meant to pay us anyway.
JAMES	What's going on?
JAN	I don't know. I don't understand this. Wait a minute. Perhaps it's just one of his tricks. You know how he likes to play.

The **Children** *all turn to the* **Stranger***.* **Kate** *steps forward.*

KATE	We've been cheated.
STRANGER	Just look at you all. No wonder my work in Hamelin is proving so easy. There are so many strings you've put in my hand. Well, let me tell you all. You have been cheated.
KATE	See!
STRANGER	That's right. Cheated. But not by me.

CHILDREN	*(together)* Yes you have . . .
	Well, who else . . .?
	Don't lie . . .
STRANGER	*(silences them)* No. Not by me. Look at what I paid you. The bits of paper. Go on, look at them.

The **Children** *scrabble round on the floor.*

STRANGER	Well?
KEVIN	Names. Signatures.
PAUL	Wait. This one says 'Councillor Fortune'.
LORNA	'Stott-Stickland'.
STRANGER	That's right. The contract from the Council. And do you know how much it's worth? Nothing.
CHILDREN	Nothing?
STRANGER	They paid us nothing. You've been cheated all right. We've been cheated. And I'll tell you who the cheats are round here. The Council. The grown-ups, *your* parents, the people who put them there. They're all cheats. They've betrayed you.
JAMES	Too right.
CHILDREN	*(variously)* Yeah . . .
	Cheats . . .
	Traitors . . .
STRANGER	But not me. I won't betray you like they did. Come with me and you can have all those things you wanted. Fame! Riches!
JAMES	You know!
STRANGER	And more. Just follow me. Trust me. I won't let you down . . .

As he speaks, the **Stranger** *leads the* **Children** *round in a wide circle, like the Ratz. The* **Stranger** *stands at the centre and spins the circle round faster and faster. The children look mesmerised. As the speed increases,* **Jan** *drops out.*

	Trust me. Trust me, Paul. That's it. Good boys. Good girls. Trust me. Your friend.
CHILDREN	*(entranced)* Our friend.
STRANGER	That's right. Follow me.

The **Stranger** *leads the* **Children** *to the edge of the Square. They follow quickly but quietly.* **Jan** *can't keep up.*

JAN *(shouts)* But wait! Wait for me! You said you were my friend.

STRANGER Remember what we said, Jan. It's the ones that smile – those are the ones you shouldn't trust. *(to the* **Children***)* Let's go!

The **Stranger** *claps his hands. The* **Children** *swarm out of the Square whooping, shrieking and chanting* 'Oy . . . oy . . . oy . . . oy . . .'.

JAN *(screams)* No-o-o-o-o!

Blackout

THE STORY

The Ratz is of course based on the legend of the Pied Piper of Hamelin. This play takes the same dilemma but places it in a more contemporary context and brings in modern social issues. You may well know the legend of the Pied Piper of Hamelin. The tale has been told and retold by generations of storytellers.

Nobody is sure how the legend began. Hamelin is a real town in Germany and there are writings on the walls of some of the old houses which tell the basic story. But are these writings based on fact or fiction? Legends like this often have an element of truth in them, and there are several interesting ideas about how the story could have started.

Perhaps the town was infested with rats, who brought disease which killed off the young children. The idea of the rats drowning themselves in the river could have come from travellers' tales of lemmings rushing over cliffs to their deaths.

Perhaps the story is based on the Children's Crusade. In 1212 about fifty thousand children from France and Germany set off towards the Holy Land, with the idea of taking it from the Muslims by the power of love, instead of military force. Most of the children ended up being captured and sold into slavery, and never returned home again.

There is another historical event which could have started the story. Early in the thirteenth century a bishop encouraged many boys from the area to move away and colonise Moravia, in the east. Perhaps the Pied Piper was one of the bishop's agents.

It is possible that all these ideas were in the mind of the original storyteller. Or perhaps a stranger really did appear in Hamelin, destroyed the rats, and then lead away the children. We will probably never know the truth about the Pied Piper.

On the following pages you will find two versions of the story: one is a modern retelling for young children; the other is a poem by Robert Browning which was first published in 1842 – only some of the verses are reproduced here. Notice the different dates at which these two versions of the Pied Piper fable claim the events in Hamelin took place. Can you explain this difference?

The Pied Piper of Hamelin

So the story goes, in the summer of 1284 the town of Hamelin was plagued by rats. The rats chased the dogs and cats. They ate the grain. They frightened the children and they left a mess. What is more, they bred like . . . rats. There were so many of them that it was impossible to walk anywhere without falling over them. The rats made everyone's life a misery.

It was not that the townspeople didn't try to get rid of rats – they did. They tried everything they could think of. They set traps. They laid poison. But everything they tried, failed.

The Mayor and the Town Council were so desperate they offered a reward to anyone who could find a solution to the problem.

Then a stranger arrived in the town. The stranger wore a coat of many colours. 'I hear there is a reward for the person who can rid this town of rats,' said the stranger. 'Anything . . . if you can help us,' said the Mayor. And the Town Council agreed.

The stranger walked to the middle of the town square and started to play a merry tune on a long pipe. The townsfolk wondered what on earth the stranger was up to. How would this behaviour rid their town of the rats?

As the stranger continued to play, the rats began to creep from their holes. The stranger started to walk through the town. He went up streets and down streets. As he passed each house, the rats left what they were doing and scampered after him.

When the stranger reached the town wall, every rat in Hamelin was behind him. The piper strode on across the fields. When he reached the river, he stepped straight into the water. Soon it came up to his knees. The tune the piper was playing grew sweeter and the rats followed straight after . . . and all were drowned.

As soon as the last rat had stopped struggling, the Mayor and townspeople of Hamelin hurried back to their homes, their dinners, their work and their games. No one even offered the piper a thank you.

The stranger put his pipe away and went to the Town Council and asked the Mayor for his reward. Now the rats were gone the Mayor saw no reason to part with the money. 'Reward?' he said. 'What reward? Leave this town now! You're not wanted here!'

The stranger left without another word. But as he walked through the streets of Hamelin, he began to play another pretty tune on his pipe. This time it was not rats which left the houses, but children. Every child in the town wanted to dance to the piper's tune and they followed him through the gate and across the meadow. This time, instead of going to the river, the piper went towards the mountain.

One small child was lame and another small child was deaf. The deaf child did not hear the piper's music and this little boy stayed at home. The lame child started to follow the piper but could not keep up with the skipping, dancing and laughing line of children. She was the only one who saw what happened. This little girl said she saw the side of the mountain open and the children follow the piper inside. By the time the lame girl got to the mountain, she could find no hole in the side of the mountain. It had disappeared.

The Mayor and the townspeople were in despair. Although they searched the mountainside, they found no door and they never saw their children again. They had disappeared just as the rats had disappeared. The people of Hamelin had only themselves to blame.

The Pied Piper of Hamelin

by Robert Browning

Hamelin Town's in Brunswick,
　By famous Hanover city;
The river Weser, deep and wide,
Washes its wall on the southern side;
A pleasanter spot you never spied;
　But, when begins my ditty,
Almost five hundred years ago,
To see the townsfolk suffer so
　From vermin, was a pity.

　Rats!
They fought the dogs, and killed the cats,
　And bit the babies in the cradles,
And ate the cheese out of the vats,
　And licked the soup from the cooks' own ladles,
Split open the kegs of salted sprats,
Made nests inside men's Sunday hats,
And even spoiled the women's chats
　By drowning their speaking
　With shrieking and squeaking
In fifty different sharps and flats.

At last the people in a body
　To the Town Hall came flocking:
''Tis clear,' cried they, 'our Mayor's a noddy;
　And as for our Corporation – shocking
To think we buy gowns lined with ermine
For dolts that can't or won't determine
What's best to rid us of our vermin!
You hope, because you're old and obese,
To find in the furry civic robe ease?
Rouse up, Sirs! Give your brains a racking
To find the remedy we're lacking,
Or, sure as fate, we'll send you packing!' . . .

'Come in!' – the Mayor cried, looking bigger:
And in did come the strangest figure!
His queer long coat from heel to head
Was half of yellow and half of red;
And he himself was tall and thin,
With sharp blue eyes, each like a pin,
And light loose hair, yet swarthy skin,
No tuft on cheek nor beard on chin,
But lips where smiles went out and in –
There was no guessing his kith and kin:
And nobody could enough admire
The tall man and his quaint attire:
Quoth one: 'It's as my great-grandsire,
Starting up at the Trump of Doom's tone,
Had walked this way from his painted tombstone!'

He advanced to the council-table:
And, 'Please your honours,' said he, 'I'm able,
By means of a secret charm to draw
    All creatures living beneath the sun,
    That creep or swim or fly or run,
After me so as you never saw!
And I chiefly use my charm
On creatures that do people harm,
The mole and toad and newt and viper;
And people call me the Pied Piper.'
(And here they noticed round his neck
    A scarf of red and yellow stripe,
To match with his coat of the self-same check;
    And at the scarf's end hung a pipe;
And his fingers, they noticed, were ever straying
As if impatient to be playing
Upon this pipe as low it dangled
Over his vesture so old-fangled.)
'Yet,' said he, 'poor piper as I am,
In Tartary I freed the Cham,
    Last June, from his huge swarms of Gnats;
I eased in Asia the Nizam
    Of a monstrous brood of vampire-bats:
And as for what your brain bewilders,
    If I can rid your town of rats
Will you give me a thousand guilders?'
'One? Fifty thousand!' – was the exclamation
Of the astonished Mayor and Corporation.

Into the street the Piper stept,
   Smiling first a little smile,
As if he knew what magic slept
   In his quiet pipe the while:
Then, like a musical adept,
To blow the pipe his lips he wrinkled,
And green and blue his sharp eyes twinkled
Like a candle-flame where salt is sprinkled;
And ere three shrill notes the pipe uttered,
You heard as if an army muttered;
And the muttering grew to a grumbling;
And the grumbling grew to a mighty rumbling;
And out of the houses the rats came tumbling.
Great rats, small rats, lean rats, brawny rats,
Brown rats, black rats, grey rats, tawny rats,
Grave old plodders, gay young friskers,
   Fathers, mothers, uncles, cousins,
Cocking tails and pricking whiskers,
   Families by tens and dozens,
Brothers, sisters, husbands, wives –
Followed the Piper for their lives.
From street to street he piped advancing,
And step for step they followed dancing,
Until they came to the river Weser
   Wherein all plunged and perished! . . .

You should have heard the Hamelin people
Ringing the bells till they rocked the steeple.
'Go,' cried the Mayor, 'and get long poles!
Poke out the nests and block up the holes!
Consult with carpenters and builders,
And leave in our town not even a trace
Of the rats!' – when suddenly, up the face
Of the Piper perked in the market-place,
with a, 'First, if you please, my thousand guilders!'

66

A thousand guilders! The Mayor looked blue;
So did the Corporation too.
For council dinners made rare havoc
With Claret, Moselle, Vin-de-Grave, Hock
And half the money would replenish
Their cellar's biggest butt with Rhenish.
To pay this sum to a wandering fellow
With a gypsy coat of red and yellow!
'Beside,' quoth the Mayor with a knowing wink,
'Our business was done at the river's brink;
We saw with our eyes the vermin sink,
And what's dead can't come to life, I think.
So, friend, we're not the folks to shrink
From the duty of giving you something for drink,
And a matter of money to put in your poke;
But as for the guilders, what we spoke
Of them, as you very well know, was in joke.
Beside, our losses have made us thrifty.
A thousand guilders! Come, take fifty!' . . .

Once more he stept into the street
    And to his lips again
    Laid his long pipe of smooth straight cane,
And ere he blew three notes (such sweet
Soft notes as yet musician's cunning
    Never gave the enraptured air)
There was a rustling that seemed like a bustling
Of merry crowds justling at pitching and hustling,
Small feet were pattering, wooden shoes clattering,
Little hands clapping and little tongues chattering,
And, like fowls in a farm yard when barley is scattering,
Out came the children running.
All the little boys and girls,
With rosy cheeks and flaxen curls,
And sparkling eyes and teeth like pearls,
Tripping and skipping, ran merrily after
The wondrous music with shouting and laughter.

The Mayor was dumb, and the Council stood
As if they were changed into blocks of wood,
Unable to move a step, or cry
To the children merrily skipping by,
– could only follow with the eye
That joyous crowd at the Piper's back.
But how the Mayor was on the rack,
and the wretched Council's bosoms beat,
As the Piper turned from the High Street
To where the Weser rolled its waters
Right in the way of their sons and daughters
However he turned from South to West,
And to Koppelberg Hill his steps addressed,
And after him the children pressed;
Great was the joy in every breast.
'He never can cross that mighty top!
He's forced to let the piping drop,
And we shall see our children stop!'
When, lo, as they reached the mountain's side,
A wondrous portal opened wide,
As if a cavern was suddenly hollowed;
And the Piper advanced and the children followed,
And when all were in to the very last,
The door in the mountain-side shut fast.

Did I say, all? No! One was lame,
    And could not dance the whole of the way;
And in after years, if you would blame
    His sadness, he was used to say –
'It's dull in our town since my playmates left!
I can't forget that I'm bereft
Of all the pleasant sights they see,
Which the Piper also promised me.
For he led us, he said, to a joyous land,
Joining the town and just at hand,
Where waters gushed and fruit-trees grew,
And flowers put forth a fairer hue,
And everything was strange and new;
The sparrows were brighter than peacocks here,
And their dogs outran our fallow deer,
And honey-bees had lost their stings,
And horses were born with eagles' wings:
And just as I became assured
My lame foot would be speedily cured,
The music stopped and I stood still,
And found myself outside the Hill,
Left alone against my will,
To go on limping as before,
And never hear of that country more!'

Alas, alas for Hamelin!
 There came into many a burgher's pate
 A text which says, that Heaven's Gate
 Opens to the Rich at as easy rate
As the needle's eye takes a camel in!
The Mayor sent East, West, North and South,
To offer the Piper, by word of mouth,
 Wherever it was men's lot to find him,
Silver and gold to his heart's content,
If he'd only return the way he went,
 And bring the children behind him.
But when they saw 'twas a lost endeavour,
And Piper and dancers were gone for ever,
They made a decree that lawyers never
 Should think their records dated duly
If, after the day of the month and year,
These words did not as well appear,
And so long after what happened here
 On the Twenty-second of July,
Thirteen hundred and seventy-six:
And the better in memory to fix
The place of the children's last retreat,
They called it, the Pied Piper's Street –
Where any one playing on pipe or tabor
Was sure for the future to lose his labour.
Nor suffered they hostelry or tavern
 To shock with mirth a street so solemn;
But opposite the place of the cavern
 They wrote the story on a column,
And on the great church-window painted
The same, to make the world acquainted
How their children were stolen away,
And there it stands to this very day.
And I must not omit to say
That in Transylvania there's a tribe
Of alien people who ascribe
The outlandish ways and dress
On which their neighbours lay such stress,
To their fathers and mothers having risen
Out of some subterranean prison
Into which they were trepanned
Long time ago in a might band
Out of Hamelin town in Brunswick land,
But how or why, they don't understand.

So, Willy, let me and you be wipers
Of scores out with all men – especially pipers!
And, whether they pipe us free, from rats or from mice,
If we've promised them aught, let us keep our promise!

DEVELOPING THE CHARACTERS

The Ratz is a play full of action and confrontation. There are several important groups of characters – the Citizens, the Councillors, the Children and the Ratz. Each group will need to work smoothly together, but it will be important that individual characters are clearly defined within each group. You will need to emphasise the chief characteristics of each group – for example, the destructive energy of the Ratz, or the pompous dignity of the Councillors – so that there is a distinctive acting style for each.

THE RATZ

The most enjoyable challenge to any production of this play is in the creation of the Ratz themselves. It is important to make them appear as original, exciting and dangerous as possible. They are fantasy characters, but it should be possible to recognise them as a nightmare version of a teenage street gang.

Each production should develop its own style of Ratz. The way they dress, make-up, move, behave and talk are all open to interpretation but the end result needs to be both exciting and frightening. While the Ratz are a genuine threat to the fabric of society, the short bursts in which they appear actually serve to inject an element of comic relief into the play: The 'Ratz in the Chamber' sequence, Scene 6, shows an act of flagrant vandalism to public property, but it is also a moment of broad slapstick comedy. The Stranger is prompted to describe this as 'entertaining' and 'a fine show'.

The Ratz bring a dangerous edge and vitality to the stultifying atmosphere of Hamelin. Their unruliness is in direct contrast to the Council, bogged down by bureaucracy and tradition.

It is important to decide at an early stage of rehearsals the way the Ratz speak. This is what really sets them apart. You will need to decide whether 'Ratspeak' is really gibberish, or a kind of backslang, whether it is simply distorted speech, or if it is the Ratz' accent which makes them sound so different. In the script all the lines to be spoken by Ratz are **printed like this**.

You may decide that the Ratz will converse with each other by a series of yells, hisses, whistles etc. You will no doubt be able to explore a whole range of unusual noises.

The Ratz may use special gestures or signs, for example when they greet each other or to express their unity and hostility to others. They will need to be very expressive in all their movements and gestures so that the audience can understand what they are trying to say. It is important that Ratspeak conveys different attitudes at different times, e.g. menace (the taking off of Becky), disgust (at seeing Jan's leg), exuberant comedy (in the Council Chamber and with the rat trap machine). You need to develop a style with elements of mime, violent ritual and circus clowning.

Ratspeak could be developed last of all, in the context of action. Before then, you need to make some important decisions:

- Is the Ratz' behaviour openly aggressive, or do they creep about in a slinky, mysterious way – like real rats?
- Are they aggressive to each other as well as to those outside their group?
- How do the Ratz live?
- What do they look like?
- What do they feed on?

Talk about these aspects of the Ratz and build up a shared image of them.

Workshop activities

1 What would it sound like if you came across the Ratz in an unlit Hamelin backstreet? Start off in a darkened room. Then try different effects – noises to terrify; noises to celebrate; noises to show fear or mistrust. Investigate different ways of raising or lowering volume – sudden silences, gradual fadings or increases of volume, sudden explosions of noise. Silences can be very effective in creating menace!

2 Use rhythm to create a sense of unity among the Ratz. Spread out round the room. Choose a rhythm of your own, and click your fingers or clap your hands in that particular beat. Move around and share your rhythm with those you meet. Try to find someone with a similar rhythm. Build as large a group of people as possible who share the same beat. Eventually, the whole group may share an identical rhythmic beat.

3 Work in a small group. Create a still picture which shows what the Citizens think the Ratz are like on their own territory. You might want to contrast this picture with another one which shows what you think the reality of their lives is like. After a few moments, bring your picture to life.

4 Work with a partner. Imagine that one of you is one of the Ratz and the other is one of the Children of Hamelin. Share with each other the good and bad things about your way of life.

5 Working in a group, create a scene which shows what life would be like if the Ratz were in charge of Hamelin. Look again at Scene 6, and see the kinds of things the Ratz seem to want. Your scene can be as exaggerated and nightmarish as you can make it. Share your scene with the rest of the group.

◁28

6 In groups, role-play the start of Scene 6 when the Ratz take over the Council Chamber. One of you could act as 'Mayor', calling on individual Ratz to present 'speeches', imitating the various Councillors: for example, one could be a very boring speaker, droning on – 'blah, blah, blah' etc.; another could act as if drunk; another could call for silence and wait for a long time as if about to say something very important – before going through a mime of a hen laying an egg.

7 Working in a group, investigate how the Ratz would act in different locations and situations e.g. in a shop, in the children's playground, in the empty Council Chamber, playing with the inventors' machine, meeting Jan alone.

8 Create a chant for the Ratz to use whenever they appear in the play.

9 Divide the group in two. Half of you are Citizens, half are Ratz. The Citizens are gathering in the Town Square when the Ratz appear. Without touching the Citizens or speaking directly to them, the Ratz should develop movements and actions which will make the Citizens begin to feel uneasy. Select the ideas which are most effective and include them in your production. You could use similar activities to unsettle your audience as they enter the performance space (hall).

THE STRANGER

This interesting character is a very mysterious figure. It is not even certain whether the Stranger is male or female. Nobody knows anything about him/her. Where does s/he come from? It is important that the person playing this part has a great deal of 'presence', is able to command attention, maintain authority and yet remain cool and detached. The Stranger addresses the audience directly, and seems to be watching and commenting on the action, whilst gaining an increasing control of events. There is something very frightening about the Stranger.

Whatever is happening, the Stranger always remains calm. We never discover this character's true nature, because this changes to suit those whom s/he is manipulating. The Stranger can be more bizarre and sinister than the Ratz, more playful than the Children, and more of a double-dealer than the Councillors. What is more, the Stranger exposes weaknesses, exploits them and finally punishes them.

Workshop activities

1   Work with a partner. Imagine that you are both Ratz. Describe to each other how the Stranger appears to you, and what power s/he seems to offer. (You might want to read Robert Browning's poem again – pages 64–69 – and see how the rats of Hamelin were affected by the music of the Pied Piper.) Repeat this exercise with a new partner, imagining that you are two of the Children of Hamelin.

2   With a partner, imagine that one of you is the Stranger and the other is a newspaper reporter who is trying to find out about the Stranger and the contract that has been made with the Council. The Stranger is not likely to give very much information away!

3   Work in a small group. You are all detectives, assigned to find out as much as possible about the Stranger and his or her previous history. Invent an appropriate background for the Stranger, and share your discoveries with the group, but do not try to explain everything away. Remember, the Stranger is mysterious and elusive.

4   Work in a group. Take it in turns to be the Stranger controlling the others who are Ratz. How does the Stranger control the unruly Ratz? How do the Ratz react to the presence of the Stranger?

THE COUNCILLORS

The members of the Town Council of Hamelin, as seen in *The Ratz*, are almost stereotypes. The roles of the Councillors give scope for some satirical character acting, but a production must also develop a dynamic cut and thrust between them. It will help to define each character if you choose one or two key attributes and exaggerate them. These attributes will be reflected in their physical appearance and behaviour: for example, the Mayor's greed may be emphasised by his size, and Councillor Witham's rigid views by his upright, military bearing. The following keynotes may help you to develop the characters of the Councillors in your improvisations and performance.

The Mayor is vain, pompous, self-satisfied, ignorant and greedy. The more he is deflated by the attacks of his opponents, the more strenuously he defends his position, and the more absurd he becomes. **Henry Stott-Stickland** can be developed as a stereotypical comic Mayor. He is pompous, self-satisfied and comically greedy.

Councillor Witham is stern, intolerant, and reactionary in his views. He sees only one solution to the problem – to 'eliminate' the Ratz. He seems not to be aware of his own obvious dishonesty and corruption.

Councillor Fitzpatrick is Witham's political ally, conservative, intolerant and easily angered.

Councillor Grahame lacks confidence and desperately wants to be respectable. She has no opinions of her own, always looks for a compromise, and is invariably the last to vote.

Councillor Phipp is an elderly eccentric whose only concern is a passionate interest in public gardens. She is completely out of touch with the real problems of Hamelin.

Councillor Fortune is the youngest member, a newcomer to the Council and rather aggressive. She is prepared to challenge everyone. Councillor Fortune is liberal in her outlook, and inclined to be sympathetic to the Ratz, but eventually signs the contract.

Councillor Worthington, although not as forceful as Councillor Fortune, is on her side. She wants to give the Ratz 'a chance'.

THE CITIZENS

Each Citizen should be as carefully differentiated as possible, so that they represent a real cross-section of the community. Their jobs, interests and affiliations will be reflected in their costumes. Some examples are given in the text, among them a policeman, a nurse and a vicar. Think of as many different roles as you need for the size of your cast – bus conductor, builder, lawyer, postman, shopkeeper, etc.

In Scene 2, the public meeting, the Citizens are not just extras with a few lines each. It is their questions and reactions which will maintain the tension in the scene, so it is very important that they are confident enough to provide their own questions and comments, and to draw the audience into a sense of participation in the meeting.

Workshop activities

The following activities should help you to create a background for the characters which will make the crowd scenes convincing. You may be able to incorporate some of the ideas that arise into your performance of the play.

1 Work with a partner. One of you, in role as a Councillor, shows a visitor round the town of Hamelin. Try to concentrate on the positive aspects of the town, and disguise or explain away the graffiti and other indications of the presence of the Ratz.

2 In small groups of Citizens, imagine that each of you has had an encounter with the Ratz. Tell the others what happened to you, and make the incident sound as terrifying as possible.

3 When you have shared your experiences, discuss as a group what you think could be done about the problem of the Ratz.

4 Set up a radio phone-in programme. Choose one or two anchor people (perhaps your teacher would like to be one of these) to chair the discussion. The others take on roles as Citizens or Councillors and can air their views about the Council, the state of the town and the Ratz. You may want to complain about the attitudes of the Town Council, and its lack of action, or you may want to defend the Council's record.

Improvisation – public meeting

The previous workshop activities should provide you with ideas, facts and opinions which you will be able to use in this improvisation. Working as a whole group, and without relying on the text, set up your own public meeting. Choose ten or a dozen people to be the Council members. Your teacher might be prepared to take on the role of the Mayor.

Use the Mayor's first speech as your starting point, and ask the Councillors to introduce themselves and give their opinions on the situation and on possible remedies. Then encourage questions from the public. Each Citizen should prepare at least one question to put to the Council. Lots of different points of view should emerge.

At any one time there should be several Citizens competing for the chance to speak during the meeting. At times they will be shouting each other down. There is nothing more unnatural than each cast member waiting for their cue, saying their learned speech and then retiring into obscurity. This scene should be like a real public meeting. The playscript gives some possible exchanges, but there is scope here to develop characters among the Citizens, each with his/her own axe to grind. Whatever happens, it is vital that the 'open' part of the meeting has a lively and spontaneous feel to it with much cut-and-thrust between Councillors and Citizens.

The Councillors, for their part, will need to react to every question in role and be consistent with the attitudes expressed in their individual speeches. An obvious split with Fortune and Worthington against all the other Councillors should quickly emerge, and this can be further developed by exchanges between Councillors whilst on the platform. It is important that the Mayor keeps control of the meeting!

It might help you to become confident in talking to an invited audience if you ask another group or class to join you in a workshop session on this section of the play. This will assist you in learning to control the development of the scene, while keeping a sense of informality and spontaneity.

After the public meeting, you might like to try this exercise: work in groups of three or four. Imagine that you are a member of the public or a Councillor. You have just come out of the meeting and are questioned on the Town Hall steps by a television reporter about what took place. Can you sum up the various arguments and opinions which were heard?

THE CHILDREN OF HAMELIN

The most naturalistic characters in the play are the Children. Like the Ratz, they have their own group loyalty, and their own codes of behaviour; they can be rough and cruel, especially to anyone who is 'different' or an 'outsider'. Even their chants and the traditional games they play have an aggressive edge. By the end of the play, they seem to have taken over much of the Ratz' behaviour, with their chant of 'Rat-attack!'

The Stranger finds it easy to exploit their mob mentality and their greed, by first making them play 'tag' with the Ratz (Scene 10), and later leading them off like a pack of rats – the Children chanting the Ratz' chant of 'Oy . . . oy . . . oy!' as they charge off in an unruly mob. Remember, today's Children are tomorrow's Citizens and Ratz.

Two Lebanese children playing with an abandoned gun they found on the streets of Beirut.

Workshop activities

1 Find out as much as you can about children's street games. You may discover some extra children's games or rhymes which you can include in the play. (*Children's Games in Street and Playground* by Iona and Peter Opie is a good reference source.) Use children's games as a basis for other songs and chants about the Ratz. These might be used to link the different scenes in the play.

2 Children who live in dangerous or violent situations have been known to use those incidents as a basis for their games. For example, the old rhyme 'Ring-o'-roses' refers to the events of the Plague. Children in Beirut have been seen playing games which mirror the violence in their city (see photo opposite). Work with a group of friends. Create a game which reflects what is happening in Hamelin – showing the nervous Councillors and Citizens, and the unexpected and hostile appearance of the Ratz. You could devise a rhyme or a rap to go with your game.

You can extend this work by transferring it to the real world. What aspects of the world around you could be represented in a game? Who would be the winners and losers? What rhymes could you invent to describe what is happening?

3 In a small group, discuss what alternative suggestions the Children of Hamelin might make for what they can buy with the money they think is coming to them from the Stranger. You could add your suggested alternatives or additions to your performance.

4 In groups of three or four, improvise a scene in which the Children talk about the disappearance of Becky and what implications it might have for them.

JAN

Jan is a difficult character to play. He is awkward, self-conscious and defensive. Because Jan is so aware of his disability, he refuses to join in and insists on being an outsider. Jan rejects even Becky's sympathy and dreads being patronised. Things are obviously no easier at home: Jan's father and dog have both gone.

It is important that the empathy between the Stranger and Jan is clearly shown. The Stranger seems to understand Jan, accepting the child on his own terms. But the Stranger also flatters and manipulates Jan, offering friendship and yet apparently deserting him at the end of the play.

Jan does not articulate his feelings. Instead he keeps them bottled up inside and in that little black book. Yes, and this is the challenge for the actor taking the role, all the sense of loss (his dog, his father, his one friend, all the Children, and the Stranger) is expressed in the final scream of 'No-o-o-o!' The last impression on the audience is that of a deserted child screaming in the darkness.

Workshop activities

1   Work with a partner. One of you take on the role of Becky, Jan's only friend; the other takes on the attitude of a schoolfriend who is hostile to Jan. Can Becky explain Jan's feelings?

2   Work in a small group. Create a series of 'photos' from the family album, which show Jan at various stages in his life. Look for clues in the text to help you.

3   In a small group, create a scene which shows Jan's fantasies and dreams of the future. Perhaps Jan dreams of success as an artist, or in some sport or physical endeavour.

4   Write an entry in Jan's black book which includes a description of the first scene of the play.

THE FUTURE OF HAMELIN

Workshop activities

1   Work in a group. Create a still picture which will show us what happened to either the Ratz or the Children after the Stranger took them away from Hamelin. You might like to read the poem again (pages 64–69), to see the suggestions there. Feel free to devise your own solutions.

2   If it was possible to stop the action of the play, could you identify a moment in which the situation might have been saved? What moment would you choose, and what steps would you take so that things might turn out in a positive way? Discuss your ideas and share them with the rest of the group.

3   Who is really responsible for what happened in Hamelin? Working in a large group, set up a tribunal, and try to establish the real underlying causes of what happened in the town. You may want to choose some people who will be members of the tribunal and others who will be defendants and witnesses. Is it possible to punish those who may be found guilty?

4   Set up another Council Meeting. This time it is five years after the incidents in the play. Show by your comments and decisions how the town of Hamelin may have been changed by these terrible events. Are the Children still missing? Are the Ratz gone for ever? Have the Councillors learned wisdom? Is Hamelin a better place to live in, or is it a dead town?

5   Write a poem which describes the events of the play. Look again at the original poem by Browning, and decide how your poem will be different. Is the moral at the end of your poem the same as that in the original?

6   Work with a partner. Imagine that many years have passed. One of you is Jan, who is now an elderly person. The other is a young friend or relation, who has heard of what occurred long ago in Hamelin. How will Jan explain what really happened? Improvise their conversation. The outcome of this activity might be included in your performance – as an 'end-piece', or epilogue.

DEVELOPING IDEAS FROM THE PLAY

THE ONES WHO SMILE . . .

The Stranger is undoubtedly the most charismatic person in *The Ratz*. You may have noticed that the Stranger seems to have an extraordinary knack of gaining the confidence and trust of anyone s/he chooses. S/he charms and manipulates most of the people s/he comes into contact with in Hamelin. But is the Stranger really very different to everyone else? Is s/he the only one who tries to manipulate others – or is it that s/he is just better at it? You might like to think about *why* the Stranger behaves as s/he does. It says in the play that the Stranger looks something like the Ratz. Was the Stranger once a Rat, perhaps?

There is a terrifying novel based on the Pied Piper story (*The Coachman Rat* by David Henry Wilson) which tells how Cinderella's coachman was transformed back into a rat at the end of the fairy story, but retained the power of human speech. Rejected by the rats and exploited by the humans, he takes terrible revenge on both communities. Do you think there could be an element of personal revenge in the Stranger's actions in *The Ratz*? Or do you think s/he is a kind of 'avenging angel', punishing the faults and weaknesses of all the characters?

The Ratz, in particular, do whatever the Stranger asks of them, giving up their individual independence and freedom of will. They become mesmerised by this charismatic character. All of us know what it is like to admire someone or to be intensely interested in something – to be, in effect, a 'follower'.

Activities

1 Look back at the play and find examples of interactions where people try to influence each other or gain power for themselves.

2 In a small group, talk about and list the interests, or individuals, people become followers of. Can you think of cases where people's interest in someone or something is so compelling that they lose the will to think or question for themselves? Talk about why you think this happens and what is good or bad about it.

3 Try a piece of writing in which someone's interest in someone, or something, is so compelling that they are completely taken over by it.

Football fans supporting their team at the 1990 World Cup.

LOVE CULT STOLE MY CHILD!

Three years ago, 17 year old Jane Mizzen went out for the evening to a meeting of the sect New Love Army. She never came home.

'Jane telephones from time to time' said mother Sally Mizzen from her home in Croydon. 'But it is like talking to a stranger. These people have brainwashed her. I'm going out of my mind with worry.'

Jane is just one of the many young people who leave home each year to join the cults and sects that have mushroomed in our cities.

A spokesman for New Love Army said in London yesterday, 'Jane is happy with us. We are her family now.'

New Love Army was started in 1972 in California by self-styled 'Universal Master' Simon Gaffa. He claims to have total control over his followers who promise absolute obedience to his 'divine commands'.

Jane Mizzen was a normal, happy teenager until she got involved with New Love Army.

THE CONTRACT

In the contract between the Stranger and the town of Hamelin, a particular deal is struck. In it, both the Stranger and the townspeople have rights and responsibilities which are closely intertwined. The Stranger has the responsibility of removing the Ratz and the right to 1,000 guilders payment. The Council has the right to have the Ratz removed and the responsibility for paying the person who achieves this. However, as the play indicates, the agreement is not really that simple. There are other issues to be considered in drawing up the contract.

Activities
1   With a partner, talk about who else or what else is affected by the contract and try writing a new one between the people of Hamelin and the Stranger.
2   There are, in a sense, other contracts in *The Ratz*. With your partner look for and talk about some of the ways in which the individuals and groups who make up the town of Hamelin are linked together by differing rights and responsibilities. You could begin by looking at:
●   Jan and the other Children
●   the Councillors and the Citizens.
3   Hold an inquest among the people of Hamelin into what went wrong and who is to blame.

'READ ALL ABOUT IT!'

Scene 7 begins with the Children of the town hawking newspapers to the Citizens seated in the audience and to the real members of the audience. The Citizens can discuss the news events with each other and with the rest of the audience. Remember that any attitudes or opinions should be consistent with those expressed in Scene 2. Starting points for discussion and reaction might be:
●   'What action should the Council take?'
●   'The Ratz have gone too far. Something must be done.'
●   'This was bound to happen, wasn't it?'
●   'Ordinary life is becoming impossible.'

At first, the Citizens seem a positive force in Hamelin. They appear to offer a challenge to an inactive and corrupt Council. However, presumably they elected the Council and must share the blame for the state of the town. If the Citizens can develop the real audience's sense of membership to the community, Wright's words 'We're all going to pay for this' should have a telling effect. The Stranger makes it clear that his/her deal is with all Hamelin, not just the Councillors. Everyone – the Councillors, the Citizens and the audience – is compromised by the Stranger in this fable of political accountability.

Activities

Work in a small group. Together, create the front page of a Hamelin newspaper. The news of the Ratz' rampage in the Council Chamber may provide the main headlines, but you may want to include pictures, an account of the Council's budget meeting, stories from local residents, police reports, Becky's disappearance and other newsworthy items. Do you want your newspaper to express the kinds of views the Citizens of Hamelin would approve of? Or is it going to be a more controversial publication?

As you work on your newspaper, you need to consider the following points:

- the title and style
- the prominence to be given to each article and picture
- the type of headline you wish to use.

Before you start, think about the technology available – from cut, paste and photocopy through to desktop publishing. There are commercial computer programs which set up text in newspaper formats. However, it is important that your group considers the different layouts and designs which would be appropriate to a newspaper of Hamelin. You can photocopy your newspapers and distribute them to the audience in Scene 7.

TRAPS FOR RATZ

In Scene 8 an inventor describes a machine designed to trap the Ratz. However, other productions could devise other machines in addition to, or instead of, the one described in the playtext: for example, a rat trap that looks like a telephone box on castors – based on the theory that Ratz cannot pass a phone box without feeling the irresistible urge to stop and vandalise it. When the telephone receiver is lifted a squirt of knock-out gas is released, allowing the capture of the Rat.

Activities

1 Work in a group. Design your own trap for the Ratz.

2 Hold a public meeting in which each inventor describes or demonstrates how their machine works. You could use these designs in your production of *The Ratz*. (You will need to make changes or additions to the script in Scenes 8 and 9, as necessary.)

3 In small groups, imagine that you are the Ratz, and show how you might prevent the traps working. Again, your ideas can be incorporated in the production.

ADDITIONAL ACTIVITIES

1   Create some of the pages of Jan's 'black book'. You may want to use some of the information in Scene 4 to help you. You could bind these together to use as a prop in your production of the play.

2   Write some of the graffiti which might appear in public places, written either by the Ratz, the Children of Hamelin or by disgusted Citizens.

3   Create a series of television news spots reflecting each public incident in the play, starting with the disappearance of Becky.

4   Design a large poster advertising the Council's reward for a trap to catch the Ratz. You can use as much of the information at the beginning of Scene 8 as you need.

5   Make a map of the town, using as much detail from the play as possible. This could be displayed with other posters depicting events or features of the town in the foyer – or in your performance space to set the atmosphere of Hamelin.

6   Compose the wording for the petition that the Citizens take round the audience in Scene 7. You could photocopy these and use the sheets in your production.

STAGING THE PLAY

THE SET

You will need to use the space you have to best advantage. You may have an elevated stage at one end of the hall with the possibility of adding rostrum blocks – or you may be able to re-arrange the staging to suit your needs. The whole hall or room can represent the topography of the town of Hamelin, with the council and East Side at opposing ends. Staging can be used as the formal debating chamber. The Citizens can sit amongst the audience.

The diagram below shows one way of staging *The Ratz*. The audience is raised on tiered seating so that the room has a 'parliamentary' feel to it. The floor space in the middle represents the Town Square and at other times the public space in the Council Chamber. For the public meeting, the Councillors could take their place on the platform at one end. This can be decorated with all the formal paraphenalia of local government. During the Council debate, Councillors can be placed on the floor of the chamber at the points marked X, with the Mayor remaining on the stage as Chairperson.

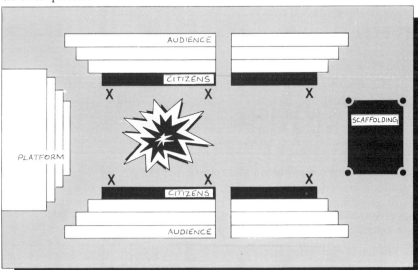

The Ratz can appear from all sides, sometimes running through the audience. If space allows it, leave gangways through the audience which become the alleys leading to and from the Town Square. You could use stage blocks, furniture etc. to build up an interesting landscape for the

Ratz to move around. It is helpful to use different levels and planes so that the Ratz can climb, jump and run – i.e. move around quickly and agilely.

You could decorate the walls of the hall with a city skyline. Washing might be hung across the corners to build up the claustrophobic atmosphere of Hamelin. Scaffolding covered with a hoarding could serve as a graffiti board and/or cover for the sound and lighting console. This end of the Square, facing directly opposite the lavishly furnished Council stage, represents the East Side of Hamelin.

The floor space in the centre could be decorated with some design. You might think of your own design that captures the atmosphere of the play to decorate the floor space with; for instance, in the first production an abstract circular design in black and white was used, giving the effect of a smashed window.

But then again you may have different ideas for how to stage a production of *The Ratz* . . .

LIGHTING

It is helpful to use lighting to help create atmosphere and different moods for different scenes. For example, the outdoor scenes featuring Jan and the children will need to be lit differently to scenes that take place in the Council Chamber. You could use flashing lights with different coloured gels in to create an exciting atmosphere whenever the Ratz appear and move around. If you can hire or borrow a strobe light, you could use this on certain occasions to create a nightmarish effect, such as when the Ratz vandalise the Council Chamber.

Warning: *Do not leave a strobe light on for long as it can cause people to feel ill. You should add a warning note to any posters or programmes stating that a strobe light is used during performance.*

Different sections of your 'acting' area can be lit differently to evoke different moods and scenes. For example, you could create a 'secretive' atmosphere for the budget fixing meeting in the Council Chamber (Scene 5) by hanging lamps over the council table and only lighting this area. As a contrast to this, the houselights could be put on for the Public Meeting, Scene 2.

Design your own lighting plot (plan), including when you need a sudden blackout and when a slow fade-out would be most appropriate. You need to decide how to light the following places to give the best possible effect:

- Town Square (Scenes 1, 4, 7, 8, 9, 10, 12, 14)
- Room in the Town Hall (Scenes 2, 3)
- Council Chamber, Town Hall (Scenes 5, 6, 11, 13).

RATMUSIC

To help the change of mood it is helpful to record a piece of music that can be played every time the Ratz appear in the auditorium. This is referred to as 'Ratmusic' or 'same three chords' in the playscript. Whatever music is chosen, it should be loud, tense and energetic.

The music you choose is part of the challenge of mounting a production of a play such as *The Ratz*. You will be establishing your own style for your own production and therefore you should choose your own music. All that you need to bear in mind is that the 'Ratmusic' presents an attitude – an attitude that is anti-establishment.

Here are some music 'styles' that might be suitable for your production:

- hip hop
- Barundi-style drumming
- thrash metal/thrash punk
- instrumental
- rap (yes, 'rap'; not rat!).

When *The Ratz* was first performed the same piece of instrumental music from a particular track was played loudly whenever the Ratz appeared. This was from 'Love Missile F111' by Sigue Sigue Sputnik. Whenever the Stranger controlled the Ratz the same three chords were played on an electronic synthesizer. These chords sounded gloomy and foreboding.

COSTUMES

Without becoming a uniform, costumes for the Ratz should emphasise the feeling that they are a gang or a tribe. When you are planning the way they dress, choose the kinds of colours and materials for their costumes which will underline the atmosphere you want to create. Will the colours be dark and sinister – purples and browns and blacks? Or will you choose brightly-painted T-shirts and leggings? Remember, the kind of clothes you choose will affect the way the Ratz move.

Don't forget to plan special make-up and hairstyles for the Ratz. You might use the kind of reflective colours used by skiers to create special effects, or wear multi-coloured wigs and special hats. (You will find some ideas on the next page.) Ask different people to design the Ratz' outfits, and choose ones which will be most effective on stage. Some materials and certain colours look very different when under stage lighting. Experiment by lighting material with different coloured lights.

The Stranger could wear a bizarre costume with striking make-up and spiky hair. His/her appearance is reminiscent of the Ratz, but more glamorous. It is essential that the Stranger looks startlingly out-of-place in the formal surroundings of the Town Hall. If possible, the Stranger should look androgynous i.e. neither male nor female.

The normal, everyday appearance of the Children should contrast with the strange costumes of the Ratz.

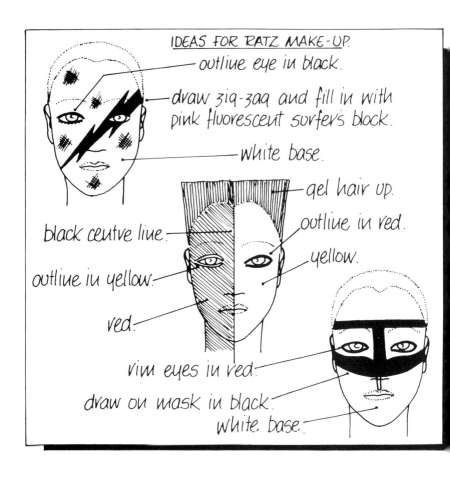

IDEAS FOR RATZ MAKE-UP.

— outline eye in black.

— draw zig-zag and fill in with pink fluorescent surfer's block.

— white base.

— gel hair up.

— outline in red.

— yellow.

black centre line.

outline in yellow.

red.

rim eyes in red.

draw on mask in black.

white base.

The Citizens should be dressed in clothes appropriate to their occupations/characters e.g. the nurse is in a nurse's uniform, the builder in overalls. The Mayor could have a chain of office. The Councillors should look their age and reflect their background. For instance, you might decide that Mr Witham would cultivate a well-groomed moustache and wear a pinstripe suit and well-polished shoes at all times; Mr Fitzpatrick would be dressed traditionally, like Witham, but perhaps with a slightly more raffish style.

But there again you may have your own ideas about all this . . .

PROPERTIES

You will need to prepare a list of properties (known as 'props') that will be needed for your production of *The Ratz*. This will include things like the Mayor's gavel (the wooden mallet he bangs to call the meeting to order), Jan's black book, aerosol spray cans, and newspapers. (See 'Read all about it!' on page 84 and number 1 under 'Additional activities', page 86.)

STAGING KEY SCENES

There are certain key scenes within the play which will require careful staging if they are to have their full dramatic effect.

Scene 1
When the Ratz first appear, they need to make an immediate visual and dramatic impact. Their costumes and make-up will obviously help with this. They could tear down signs, play with street furniture and charge in amongst the audience. One of the Ratz could spray 'THE RATZ' over a wall (actually, on a large sheet of paper or cardboard against a wall or scaffolding hoarding) with an aerosol. This graffiti can remain throughout the rest of the performance as a reminder of the Ratz' presence in the town.

Devise the way in which the Ratz manage to carry out the 'taking off' of Becky. Ask yourselves, 'Is Becky abducted or does she go willingly?' When you have decided upon an answer, then you should think about how the Ratz will separate Becky from Jan and carry her off.

One suggestion for staging this short episode is for the Ratz to form two circles around Becky, one inside the other. They rotate in different directions – one clockwise and the other anticlockwise.

Scene 2
In performing the play, the Citizens can be spread among the real audience – either from the very beginning or they can arrive at the start of this scene as if they have just arrived for the Public Meeting. If you decide to bring them in after the first scene, make sure that seats are kept for them among the audience.

As the houselights come back on at the start of Scene 2, the Citizens should try to engage the members of the audience near them in discussion and speculation about the state of affairs in Hamelin. They might raise points such as:

- the terrible problems created by the Ratz
- any incidents they have witnessed or been involved in
- the need for the Council to take urgent action
- the attitudes and personalities of some of the Councillors
- what is likely to take place at the meeting
- the terrible story of the young girl kidnapped by the Ratz.

By the time the Councillors have taken their seats, there should be a buzz of conversation in the hall. Throughout the meeting the Citizens need to be an active audience, showing their reactions with cheers, boos and assorted comments. They should try to involve the real audience in what is happening, by commenting and exchanging opinions on what has been said. Cries of 'Speak up' for quieter speakers will help to build up a powerful atmosphere – the noisier the better! But remember, the Mayor must be allowed to maintain order. The person playing the Mayor might do this with a gavel, handbell or loud buzzer.

When the Mayor asks for order, the Councillors could 'freeze' – for a moment. The Councillors should find an attitude at the table which typifies their character and relationship to both the other Councillors and the audience: you might look very pompous and self-important; you might be very aware of the audience; or you might be totally absorbed in your own notes. Hold your position for a moment or two – so that the audience can begin to register your attitude. This gives the scene a strong starting point.

Scene 3

It may help to stress the impression created by the Stranger's costume and make-up in the formal surroundings of the Town Hall if the Councillors remain on stage throughout this scene – 'frozen' at the table.

Scene 5

You might repeat the idea of the 'frozen moment' as suggested for Scene 2 at the beginning of this scene. For those of you playing Councillors, will your attitude to your colleagues be different from those you displayed at the start of Scene 2?

If the play is staged 'in the round', the Councillors could stand facing each other down each side of the room, with the Mayor in a chair at one end. Councillors Fortune and Worthington should stand next to each other.

Scene 6

When the Ratz take over the Council Chamber, there are many things they can do to mock the actual town council. Here are some suggestions, but you may be able to think of your own:

- try on robes and model them, using the Council table as a catwalk
- unroll official scrolls and make paper darts/aeroplanes which they throw around
- tear pages out of books and screw them up for paper ball fights, and to throw at the audience
- pick up quills from the Council table, put them in their headbands and imitate American Indians
- point out portraits on the walls and imitate the self-important subjects.